A North Country Maid

by Mary Craddock

You would expect any book about life in a Durham mining village during the terrible industrial Depression of the inter-war years to be deservedly bitter and bleak. But not this one. This touching, affectionate and funny account of what it was like to grow up in those times pulls no punches, but social conditions, including the growth of political consciousness, are only one part of a book about real human beings.

'My father,' says Mary Craddock, 'was an old miner, crippled with rheumatism, squat and tetchy, but with a wonderful gift of the gab . . . to me, at first, he was just "Father", a dim figure of authority and uncertain temper . . .' but slowly he came alive to her, as he does to the reader, as a man of fine and proud spirit and as a man of intelligence, clever at school as a boy, and one with his own wistful longing for what he might have been if only he'd been given a chance . . . 'A *proper* scholar, like those chaps with gowns on . . .'

Instead, throughout the ten years of the book, he was continually unemployed, on the dole, to be rewarded at the end with a job – temporary, of course – as a road-sweeper. During all of this time real poverty and the shameful Means Test were all part of everyday reality for his children, who nevertheless knew many joys as well as sorrows.

His daughter, blessed with the opportunities he never had, gives a glowing description of those years and of all the people who inhabited them, using a witty and beautiful turn of phrase that goes right to the heart of the life she describes.

'**Authentic. A story to read and read again,**' said the *Daily Express*. Said Maurice Wiggin in *The Bookman:* '**I would be very proud to have written this book.**'

Mary Craddock

A
North Country
Maid

GEORGE MANN of MAIDSTONE

A NORTH COUNTRY MAID

Mary Craddock

Copyright © Mary Craddock 1960

First published by Hutchinson and Company (Publishers) Ltd
1960

First published by George Mann 1995

ISBN 0 7041 0258 7

Printed and bound in the United Kingdom by
The Longdunn Press Ltd, Bristol,
and Published by George Mann
of PO Box 22
MAIDSTONE
in the English County of Kent

A NORTH COUNTRY MAID

1. Avelstan

It was not until I was an undergraduate, forced to read *Morte d'Arthur* right through, that I received a blinding flash of illumination. Avalon – where there's neither mist nor snow, where all is peace and beauty – why it was none other than Avelstan. I closed the book and stared back down the years.

My father was an old miner, crippled with rheumatism, squat and tetchy, but with a wonderful gift of the gab. Since the pit had closed ten years before, he'd been unable to find employment, and had gone 'on the Means Test'. Now, I can understand the fineness of his spirit, the ever renewed miracle of his cheerfulness, and I can guess at the long sleepless nights, when his children had somehow been fed and were fast asleep, and he was able to confide his helplessness to the empty night. But then, to me, a child of twelve, he was just 'father' – a dim figure of authority and uncertain temper. Vaguely I distrusted him. Other children's fathers worked. Why didn't he? And when Mother did all the work in the house, why should he be the boss? Why should everyone defer to him – my mother setting the example, even to Jane, the wage-earner? Hadn't this attitude been partly responsible for Fred's rebellion and rejection?

So I was sullen to Father, reserving my cuddles and childish

7

intimacies for Mother, who was too busy to pay attention, especially during the school holidays.

I was mooning in the living-room one wet September morning, nose pressed against the pane, frowning at the garden. Had it been fine, Father would have been tending his vegetables or, more likely, leaning over the gate talking to his unemployed cronies. For hours they would gas there, nodding their heads in solemn agreement, putting the world to rights before they went on with the noble task of weeding the cabbage patch.

Father was sitting in his usual chair, chewing the stem of his old clay pipe, occasionally leaning forward to spit into the fire. I will say this – he was a grand fireman. In the old days when he'd been working – a period so vague to me that it was mostly hearsay – and the load of coal arrived which was part of a miner's wages, he had personally shovelled it into the coal-house, checking for roundies with an expert eye. When he'd gone on the means test he had to forage for coal – a task he loathed. Up at the colliery he sometimes bought a load cheap and when it arrived it was always mostly slack and dust. He never touched this coal himself, but stood wearing a bitter expression, humming 'I know that my redeemer liveth' while the sacks of rubbish were poured through the hatch directly into the coal-house. He was caustic about the quality of this 'pitman's' coal, but he certainly knew how to extract the last ounce of energy from it, slack or no slack.

Our little tabby cat, thin but wiry, leapt on to his lap, purring loudly. Usually Father threw it from him but this time he allowed it to nestle, stroking it absently. Man, cat and fire made such a harmonious picture in contrast to the dreary drizzle of my window view, that I gradually drew nearer, until I was leaning against the wooden armchair, stroking the cat as it lay blissfully on Father's lap.

Mother had taken Alice to Mrs. Price's, the woman who made over old dresses, so for once the house was empty, except for Father and me. I felt an unaccustomed shyness as I furtively stroked the tabby. The cheap clock ticked loudly from the wooden mantelpiece above the range, and I stared into the fire, hypnotized by the little gas bubbles on the grate.

'Father,' I asked idly. 'Have you always lived here?' For I couldn't imagine him in any other place save this kitchen, or in any other chair but this big wooden armchair near the fire.

'Eh?' he said. 'What's that, lass?'

I had disturbed his reverie. I repeated the question, feeling slightly foolish, bored already. I hadn't really been interested. But the effect on Father was magical. He threw me a fine look from his pale blue eyes and his shoulders straightened under the shabby cardigan.

'Always lived here? Me? I should think not,' he said indignantly.

There was a silence which I was afraid to interrupt. Nervously I picked at a scab that had formed on my knee.

Father spoke so gently that he might have been speaking to himself – or rather to a younger, more tender self.

'Nay, lass. I wasn't born in Rainton. I was born in Avelstan.'

His voice, normally raucous as an old crow's, caressed the word, 'Avelstan'.

I took the word into my mind and savoured it on my tongue. It had the magic of all things barely understood but carrying with them touches of grandeur. It reminded me of all my special things – the beckoning lure of fair lights in the distance – the moment when the gas chandelier was lit at school – my secret place in the garden between the currant bushes – the old ruined tower across the fields. And it had in it the beauty of touch, too. It was like drinking milk warm from the cow, like the tiny prickles that drizzle makes on your face, like the touch of velvet on Mother's best hat. The word became mine. I looked with interest at my father. Then another aspect struck me. 'You were *born* there?' I asked with awe.

Somehow it had never occurred to me that Father had ever been born. That meant that he must have been a baby, a monkey-faced squalling thing with petal curling fingers. That he must have been a child going to school like me. That he must have been a young man courting my mother – a younger fresher Mother who had perhaps curled her hair with tongs and worn crisp white blouses to meet my father.

I needed to think about this. I looked at my father's face intently, observing the thin soft grey hair, the huge ears, the round pink face with the grizzly bristles and drooping moustache, the pale blue eyes scarcely visible beneath the shaggy brows, and the fine arched nose which gave character and dignity to the face. I tried to see in that face traces of his former selves, but I couldn't. This face before me was *real*, it couldn't have been anything else. It was the face of my father, un-changing, set in the mould. Then suddenly the face which I had been scrutinizing so closely, moved, the mouth opened, the head nodded and I was gazing at a bright blue eye close to mine. The other was closed in a wink. My father was laughing.

'The day I was born,' he said gleefully, 'old Farmer Stevie's cow had a two-headed calf. Aye – they'll never forget that day in Avelstan.'

Basking in vicarious fame, I smiled tenderly at my father.

'Do they still remember you there then?'

'Remember me? They'll never forget Joseph Craddock in Avelstan. Born the same day as the two-headed calf.'

He leaned forward heavily and pushed a paper spill through the grate bars, then leaned back, arms crossed over his chest, puffing mightily.

'What was it like, Da? In Avelstan.'

Cautiously I spoke the name aloud for the first time. I was fixing my signature to the place – making it mine.

'Oh, it was a grand place, Avelstan. A little country village, you know. It was set up a height on a hill and a little row of cottages led down the bank to the stream yonder.'

His face had softened as he spoke, misting the contours.

'Did it have a school, Father?'

'That it did – and a village green where all the bairns used to play of an evening. And we had a grand schoolmaster. Mr. Teasdale the schoolmaster – I mind him well.'

'What was he like?'

'Oh, a clever chap him. Mind he was. And a brisk, noble-looking chap at that. The books he had – he had an attic full of them. Many an afternoon I've spent up in that attic.'

Father suddenly flashed me a shrewd look. My naked face and concentrated gaze must have reassured him of my interest. His voice dripped honey.

'Now I'll tell you a funny thing.'

Nobody knew better than my father the value of a dramatic pause.

'Uh huh?'

'Ye've heard tell of Shakespeare?' Of course I had.

'Well – one day I was up in the attic, clearing it up a bit you know, when I came across this box.'

I hardly dared breathe.

'I opened it up with my penknife, and it was chock-a-block. Full to the brim.'

'What of, Father?'

He drew in a deep breath and expelled it with a pop.

'Papers,' he said significantly. 'Thick papers.'

Not unnaturally, I felt disappointed. Quick to sense this, Father touched my arm with a horny finger.

'And I'll tell you a funny thing,' he said. 'The s's was all f's.'

I was gratifyingly startled. It was as though I'd been given a present, of whose value I was uncertain, except that it was beyond riches. Father sat very still, rapt with the long-ago sense of discovery. My heart thumped with the mystery.

'What became of them papers I never heard tell,' he said, 'but I'll never forget that day. Thick papers with a lot of writing on – and the s's was all f's.'

I couldn't have this happiness destroyed so soon.

'Father,' I cried reproachfully. 'Why didn't you keep them?'

'Eh? What's that? Oh – that wouldn't have done at all. They didn't belong to me. Besides there was always something happening to take your attention in Avelstan – you know the life lads lead.'

I thought about the boys I knew, always knocking each other about or huddling over marbles in mysterious contemplation. I thought about the games they played in the back streets, about the intensive compulsion of gang loyalty. I understood, but I felt bitter against the boy who had been my father, the boy who had glimpsed mystery and let it slip through his fingers.

'What did you do there?' I asked sulkily.

'Oh, there was always plenty to do. Climb trees, go birds nesting, fish for tiddlers.'

My fingers found the scab again, my attention wandered.

'We had a famous pond at Avelstan, you know. The duck pond. Everybody used to meet either up at the duck pond or down by the bridge.'

He began to sing, beating time with his gnarled old hands against the wooden arms of the chair:

> 'Oh, Jemima, look at your Uncle Jim
> He's in the duck-pond learning how to swim
> First he does the breast stroke, then he does the glide
> Now he's in the water, swimming against the tide.'

I liked the jaunty rhythm and joined in the song.

'What was so special about the duck pond?'

'Well, now, what do you think a duck pond is, lass?'

I thought, suspecting a catch. 'A pond where ducks swim,' I offered in my pupil's voice.

'Well, you're wrong, you see,' said Father triumphantly. 'A duck pond is where people were ducked.'

I giggled, not believing him, but joying in the absurdity of the notion.

'Aye,' said Father triumphantly, eyes rolling comically in the way they did when he'd scored a point, 'aye, you had to mind your p's and q's in Avelstan, or you were for the duck pond.'

He was not going to gain his victory so easily. He must give details, examples, reasons before I surrendered to this pleasing fantasy.

'But *who* was ducked, Father? And who decided what they were going to be ducked for?' I asked sternly.

Father checked his gleeful contortions and became solemn.

'Why it all depended, you see, on what they'd done.'

'Like what, for instance?'

'Like – oh – gossiping, or telling tales – or asking too many questions.'

I puffed my cheeks imitatively in a hoot of derision. This was the usual adult's trick of putting me in my place.

'Were *you* ever ducked?' I asked quickly, feeling cunning.

Father responded as I'd anticipated.

'That I wasn't. Never. Not, mind you, that I never did anything wrong. Far from it. I was always up to some devilment – as a lad, that was,' he added quickly, eyeing me with caution.

'But did you ever help to duck anybody?'

I was, like all children, single-track minded.

Father spat with scientific accuracy at an incautious flame.

'Aye, there was one time,' he began, 'I'll never forget. You see, we had a famous stone in Avelstan. Matter of fact some did say that was how Avelstan got its name. Some saint or something of that sort used to preach there in olden days. It was a great big stone standing by the roadside just outside the village.'

'What was the saint's name?'

'Oh – some did say it was St. Ive – but then nobody really knew, you know. It was far too long ago. Well – some blokes high up in the Church, bishops and that, come to hear tell of this stone, and they got the idea they would hold a service there, you see, in honour of this saint, like.

'Oh, a grand do it was going to be, an all. The Bishop of Oldchester himself was going to preach and all the toffs was coming to hear him.

'Now just before the great day, the bishop was making a speech in Oldchester and he made a remark about "ignorant peasants". That put the backs of the common people up good and proper. Oh, the talk there was about that speech in Avelstan! My people kept the pub there, you ken, so I heard all the crack.'

Father's eyes rounded and he laughed delightedly as he re-lived the exciting moment.

'What a fuss there was! Mr. Teasdale the schoolmaster had taken offence – it was like a reflection on him you see – and everybody was boasting how many books they had in the house – not counting bibles. For eddication was a highly thought of thing in Avelstan,' he said solemnly. 'Highly thought of indeed. And the bishop said as much as we couldn't read.' He paused to let the enormity of the crime sink in.

'Is that the man who was going to preach at the stone?'

'The same fella, the very next week. That was the tragedy of it, you see.'

I didn't follow this, and waited expectantly.

'Noo when the great day arrived, we were holding a protest meeting in the school-house. We all decided that we wouldn't turn up for the service. Aye,' he chuckled, 'I felt sorry for the vicar, Mr. Simpson. He didn't know which way to turn. He kept taking members of his congregation aside trying to get them to promise to go to the service, threatening them with hell-fire and I divent know what, but they weren't having any. He was outvoted at the meeting.'

At this evidence of democracy in action, Father shook his head pityingly. 'Poor old Simpson hadn't a chance. Clean outvoted. Unanimous.'

'Is that all that happened?' I asked, disappointed. 'Did you just stay away?' My young blood wanted action, worthy of the people of Avelstan.

'That would have been all if the schoolmaster had had his way. Everything dignified. He was a great one for dignity, was Mr. Teasdale.'

'But what happened?' I prompted, scenting satisfaction.

'Well, you see, I wasn't at the meeting all the time. I was sent to the pub for sandwiches and I was on me way to the school-house with a plateful in each hand when I saw this fella standing by the duck pond. He was tall and lanky, and he had on one of them big pork-pie hats and a collar turned round the wrong way. I could see he was a toff, so I off and away to the school-house as fast as I could.

' "The bishop's come," I yelled at the door. "And he's standing by himself looking at the duck pond."

' "Where's the rest of the party?" asked Mr. Teasdale.

'Now that was a funny thing, if you come to think. What was the bishop doing there by himself? Where was all the choirboys and parsons and such like? Everybody looked disappointed. They'd been wound up, you see, by the suddenness of it. Then somebody caught sight of the vicar.

' "Here," he shouts. "You know what the bishop looks like. Tell us if that's him." '

'Well, they all push the vicar out of the door and he creeps round shamefaced to spy on this stranger. He daresn't do any other, you see – the people of Avelstan being his flock.

'As soon as he sets eyes on the fella he jumps up and darts back into the school-house, terrified.

' "It's him," he whimpers. "I've seen him preach in the cathedral. You mustn't do anything to him now." '

'But that was enough for the meeting. The women were the worst – they always are. They all rushed out howling with rage, and grabbed ahold of him with their big brawny arms, and before you knew it, there was the bishop spluttering in the duck pond.'

A look of unholy glee came into Father's face.

'Drenched he was, soaked to the skin.'

I was pleasurably shocked.

'But what *was* the bishop doing there by himself?' I asked, puzzled. 'Where were the choirboys and things?'

I had as vague an idea of ecclesiastical hierarchy as my father.

Father started to shake again.

'Oh – they got ahold of the wrong fella,' he said. 'It wasn't the bishop at all – it was the dean. Parson was wrong, you see. He was too far down the scale to know the difference. It takes a scholar, you see, to know a thing like that.'

A meditative gleam came into his eyes.

'Aye, I felt sorry for him, never the same chap after that experience. Couldn't hold his head up in church. He left soon after that and we got another parson,' he added with satisfaction. 'It would never do, you know, for the folks of Avelstan to have an *ignorant* parson.'

'Were they all clever in the village, then?'

'Smart as mustard.'

'Were you clever as a lad?'

Father looked at me impressively. 'I was the cleverest scholar,' he said slowly, 'that Mr. Teasdale had ever had. Told my mother so himself. Frequently. Said I'd go far.'

I felt a shamed incredulity, but didn't reply out of delicacy. A look of bitterness came into my father's face. The fire had gone out of him and he slumped in his chair, the clay pipe nearly slipping out of his crooked fingers.

He held one of his hands out as straight as he could, examining it dispassionately. It was a miner's hand, scarred and misshapen, with lines etched in that blue trade-mark which handling coal leaves on the skin. Rheumatism had twisted the bones, causing the knuckles to stand out sharply, and the fingers to turn off uselessly at an angle. The hand wouldn't straighten.

'I can barely hold a pen now,' he muttered, 'but as a boy I had a lovely copperplate hand.'

'Why didn't you stay on at school, Da?' I asked timidly.

That roused him. He looked at me as if aware for the first time of my presence.

'I left Avelstan.'

To me, it was as though he'd left paradise. I sat very still, not able to share my father's emotion, not daring to intrude on it. The kitten began to play with a straggle of wool hanging from Father's cardigan, and I didn't even check it. Questions turned in my head, but I didn't give them tongue. My foot went to sleep and I concentrated on the tingles as a release.

Father leaned forward and lit another spill, which flared over his face as he relit his pipe.

'Aye,' he said at length. 'My father took a stroke and was dead inside a week. Never regained his speech. And he left my mother nowt bar a big family to keep. Common enough thing, but it meant we had to leave Avelstan and settle elsewhere.'

Elsewhere – any place that was not Avelstan must have been elsewhere. To this nameless place they had come and there Father found work in the pits.

'How old were you when you started work?' I asked.

'Fourteen, lass, and I worked in the pits for forty years.'

It sounded like a sentence of lifetime imprisonment.

'Did you like it?' My question sounded inadequate even to me.

'Well, you know what lads are. It was a man's life and I had some pocket money to spend. I thought I was a masher.'

He surveyed me through the thick rank smoke set up by his clay pipe, cocking his head on one side.

'Did you ever go back?' I whispered.

'Never from that day to this.'

This appalled me. I was grasping at a dream. Avelstan must be accessible otherwise nothing seemed worth while. Everything that had been real threatened to tumble round my buzzing head. I cast a wild glance at my father and found in him a monumental sanity, the sad wisdom of acceptance.

'It does no good going back, lass,' he explained kindly. 'But there's one thing I learned while I was there.'

I waited expectantly under Father's eye.

'The value of eddication.'

A shy smile appeared unexpectedly under his sprawly grey moustache.

'I mind when I was a nipper. Me mother took me up to Oldchester for the day – for a treat, you see. I'd been top of the class and she took me to see the river and the cathedral. Well, I was swelled headed with all the fuss – natural enough – and I happened to catch sight of these blokes walking about with great flappy black things on. I was struck with this, you see, so I asked my mother what it could be.

' "Them's scholars, Joe," she says to me. "They belong the University."

' "But I'm a scholar," I says. "Mr. Teasdale says I'm the best scholar he ever had." '

Father chuckled with tenderness, then turned to me with unexpectedly revealing candour.

'Mind, lass, that's one thing I'd dearly like to have been. A proper scholar, like them chaps with gowns on, walking about the streets of Oldchester.'

I was filled with missionary fervour. There was one thing I could do to repay my father for that precious glimpse of Avelstan. I could go in for 'eddication', I could wear a gown in Oldchester.

'Stick in at school, lass,' said Father gently. 'Just do the best you can.'

That was the only legacy I received from Father, an ingrained respect for 'eddicated folks'.

Or had he given me something deeper – a defence against Utopianism? For Avelstan existed – there was no necessity to invent it. It was indissolubly linked in my mind with the box of papers, where the s's were all f's, and I preserved the mystery until it became a talisman in my mind, a touchstone of wonder that made me a child again.

2. The Family

M Y first conscious memory is of grasping the edge of the tin bath and hauling myself up to look at the fire. Then I was aware of the roughness of the towel and the vigour of my mother's hands on my body.

The fire was the centre of home, and Mother was its presiding deity. She was always doing something at the hearth – black-leading the grate, putting dough to rise at the fireside, raking coals under the oven or hanging clothes on the huge clothes-horse, to dry round the fire. When her work was done she'd sit with her feet on the polished fender, mending or sewing. Father's wooden armchair stood to the left of the fireplace and nobody else ever sat in it, even the cat.

Every evening when Father came back from the pit, he'd put his bait tin and flask on the table, then strip to the waist and have his tub-wash in the flickering firelight. Mother would take a scrubbing brush to his back and the rhythm of her strokes and the smell of carbolic had a special privileged meaning to me. The memory was fleeting, for Father's pit, the Daisy, laid him off when I was very young, so that later I didn't know whether I had actually experienced the evening bath rites or that when Fred, my eldest brother, bathed in front of the fire, I wasn't superimposing this picture falsely on my earlier memories of Father's hewing days.

But the memory of the taste of bait tin bread and cold sweet tea from the pit flask was too real and intensely enjoyed ever to have been imagined. It was my special private pleasure, my first insight into the warm magic of the miner's life. The bread was usually stale and crispy, its sugar coating mingling with the masculine taste of pit dust, making it mysterious and delicious, heavy with symbolism. The cold sugared tea, too, was syrupy, as if it had been transmuted at lower levels into the drink of gnomes. Nothing has ever equalled the flavour of that pitman's fare.

Gradually I became aware of people moving in and about the house, and through them, of the house itself. My horizon widened from the edge of the pram to the ceiling of the middle room, with the laths showing through its fascinating cracks and flakes. Then I learnt to gauge the extent of the horse-hair sofa in front of the window. My curiosity extended to the rag mats on the stone-flagged kitchen floor, and I adventured towards the plump solidity of the table legs, which lurked dangerously beneath the heavy plush tablecloth. And one day I discovered my sister.

Alice, a few years older than I, looked after me with absorbed solemnity. It was a day in autumn when she invaded my consciousness and became something other than a dim figure at the edge of my push chair. We were standing on the path just beyond the railway gates. I had gaiters on my legs and I was pushing against the cold wind, burrowing my face in the folds of Alice's coat. Then we stopped. Alice made soothing noises and did something with my cold hands. She was putting them inside warm black cotton gloves – warm with her body heat. I looked at Alice's fresh face and hanging yellow hair and I knew that she was putting *her* gloves on *my* fingers, and that she was close to me, to be singled out from the maze of giant shapes that clutched at me and whose hands were eager to touch me. I put my hand in Alice's as a spontaneous gesture of trust, and after that she was always special to me.

Through Alice I became aware of the rest of the family. There was Fred, a gruff-voiced quick-moving figure, who used to stand in the scullery, stripped to the waist, flexing his muscles and grasping for heavy objects to try his strength. I kept out of his way because if he saw me he'd lift me high up over his head, drowning my squeals in his throaty laughter. When he shouted the others ran, bringing him food or boots, or filling the big kettle that spat sizzling on to the fire. Fred terrified me.

Then there was Jane, an awesome grown-up who had spent two

years at a training college and who came and went not in a fixed routine, but at bewildering intervals, obeying a rhythm beyond that of the family, which pulsed through all our lives. She had plump white hands that touched softly and in turn I loved to touch her legs, tightly trapped in spiders' webs. When I stroked her she'd lift me on her lap and let me play with her hanging beads, but I must never twine my fingers in her hair or touch the thick bun pinned carefully at the nape of her neck. She had a lovely creamy smell that delighted me as much as the butterfly kisses she made on my cheek with her eyelashes. When she came home she'd bring me little chocolate men or fish, or a packet of hundreds-and-thousands. Sometimes she showed me books of pictures and told me stories that she told the 'other children', who took her from me.

Then there was my brother Ted, the young lad to whom I gave my heart. He was like a whirlwind to me; he smelt of apples and the wind in autumn. He had thick curly hair that he'd let me tug when he played with me. Sometimes Ted used to take me to his hut at the bottom of the garden, carrying me high on his shoulders, so that I queened it over the mimulus and poppies, the roses and leeks, the stocks and pansies – from a dizzy height. He'd bear me safely past the chicken coop and ease me gently down on to his work bench.

There was one tiny window in Ted's cree, with blobs of tar fixed in eternal trickles. Inside, the hut smelt of leather and oil, wood and springs; a heavy masculine mixture that I sucked on in ecstasy. Ted's bicycle rag had glory for me and I chewed it surreptitiously until he caught me. Wonderful things happened in Ted's shed. He was for ever taking things to bits – an old clock or watch, a doll whose eyes had opened and shut in infuriating mystery, a toy engine, a bicycle wheel. From my vantage point all I could ever see was the top of Ted's springing hair and only hear his intent breathing. I was content to be there, sucking whatever my groping fingers presented to my eager mouth, happy only to exist in Ted's cree, ecstatic if he let me push dandelion leaves through the wire netting of his rabbit hutch, moaning with pleasure if he let me feel its silky angora fur.

Ted loved to experiment and once, by candle flame, he fried some chips in a tin lid. I ate them obediently, enjoying the candle-grease flavour, but was utterly sick afterwards. Mother wiped me clean and put on a fresh bib, but she spoke so sharply to Ted that he didn't take me back to his cree for a long time afterwards. I took to following him about, which annoyed him, especially if the lads wanted him to go out with them. They'd shout at me and threaten to throw sticks, so I was driven back to the garden gate where I'd wait tearfully for Ted's return, unless I was discovered and taken indoors.

In my infancy Father was to me merely a moustache and a smell of twist baccy. He used to give me a ride by jogging me on his boot sometimes, but he never really penetrated my world. Nor did Mother. If Father was nothing, she was everything and so equally unknowable. She had as many forms as Proteus, each associated with a different smell, that spread from her to the whole house. There was the soapy, sneezy smell of washing day, marked by the thumping in the poss-tub, the prickly, dry smell of ironing day when the fire was big and crackling, the crisp smell of baking day, when it was my pleasure to prod holes through the crust on the rising dough, the slightly acid smell of cleaning day and the scenty soap smell of Sunday, when Mother appeared in her best dress and modesty vest, and had her fringe prinked into curls.

I learnt many things before I went to school. I learnt to go to Nicholson's farm over the road with the tin can for warm milk, which I surreptitiously sipped on the way home. I learnt to distinguish between the Black Rows where the miners lived, and the streets of stone houses in the rest of Rainton. I learnt how to tell the time by the Store clock, never to go on my own past either the railway bridge or the crossing, and to mind the buses when I crossed the road.

For at five I could run errands. If the butcher caught sight of me he'd serve me out of turn and would always ask me what I wanted with an air of solemn expectation, although my purchases never varied. 'Two penn'orth of pease pudding and a pound of potted meat please,' was all I was entrusted with at that time.

I had difficulty in the grocery store, because the marble counter towered above my head, and all the assistant could see was one of my hands clutching the edge while the other rapped in a peremptory manner, making a fine sound on the marble. He would lean over and discover me standing on tiptoe, pink with effort, muttering over and over again like a liturgy, 'An *end* of ham *shank* for the *broth* pan please.'

Threading through all this knowledge of practical affairs was a deeper awareness of fate. It took several forms, from touching wood to consulting visiting gipsies, but it was there, ineffable, imponderable. Father was sceptical of all superstitions but Mother and, to some extent Jane, believed that some people had 'the gift'.

The herbalist's shop, which stood over the railway gates and therefore lay beyond my unattended province, was a constant source of wonder and excitement. Here you could buy herbs for every ailment under the sun. People would go there furtively, usually after dark, and emerge clutching little brown paper packets with guilty triumph. His shop was long, narrow and dark. Strangely coloured liquids in enormous bottles caught what light there was, and a hundred tiny drawers concealed the herbs from the eyes of the curious. It was a secretive shop that smelt of Time itself. It is a dim memory to me now: it seemed to disappear about the time my mother stopped wearing those black spotted veils that tucked under her chin, sealing her off in mystery.

Ganny Wilson, however, seemed to live for ever. She lived at the end of a row of slums at the bottom of Rainton bank. For some reason the slums were below ground level, but Ganny Wilson's house stood at street level, so when the slums were demolished her house was spared. At least that was the official reason given, but to those who knew Ganny Wilson the real reason was that nobody dared interfere with her. She had a wild appearance which supported her claim to read the future. Going into her shop was like descending into the underworld.

It was inexpressibly tiny and cluttered up with useless stock, all in inextricable confusion. Cards of buttons would be next to ripe cheese, carnival hats on top of moulding jars of jam, paraffin oil next to open tins of forgotten biscuits, and jars of highly coloured sweets everywhere. When you pushed down the sneck, a bell would ring and the door creaked open. You waited inside the bulging shop until eventually you heard a shuffling slither, then Ganny Wilson would appear, pushing aside the old mat that hung over an alcove leading to her private lair. Her matted grey hair kept escaping from its hairpins, to be pushed back with an habitual gesture of her bony hands. She was excessively thin and stooped so that her arms hung unnaturally long. Her eyes seemed to see everything, their constant expression conveying an appraisal so sardonic that it cut through your protecting layers of hypocrisy and self-approval, to the poor little thing that you really were. She wore shapeless colourless things that hung and rustled as she moved. Likely she slept in them. When you saw her outside, wandering over the bogs and marshes beside the old line, she always had an old shawl over her head. Sometimes she burnt things outside, feeding the flames with little twigs she'd collected, absorbed in her private ritual.

Everybody bought oddments from her shop, partly because she was always open for custom, unlike the Stores, and partly because it was tacitly considered best to keep on the right side of a body like Ganny Wilson. The old wives maintained that she had second sight and would sometimes read the teacups for you.

Later, when we were on the Means Test and Fred talked wildly of emigrating, Mother was worrying herself sick, so Jane took her along to see Ganny Wilson, unknown to Father, who would have been furious. They took along with them a penknife belonging to Fred and I can remember the row there was when he realized he'd lost it.

'You can't leave a thing about in this damned house,' he bellowed. 'Look for it, can't you? It's got to be somewhere.'

So we turned the house upside down, Mother included, but the pen-knife never turned up. Presumably they'd left it at Ganny Wilson's and daren't go back for it.

Alice told me in bed one night that Ganny had laughed at the very idea of Fred's leaving the country. It was all fancy talk, to look big.

'But she said we'd never have any good of him,' she added, tight lipped. 'And that's true enough. We have to beware of a dark woman. I shouldn't be surprised if he gets married and leaves us flat.'

That was the great betrayal. The family came first and it was the bounden duty of the eldest to see the younger ones through.

'What did they take the penknife for?' I whispered.

'So that Ganny Wilson could go into a trance.'

After imparting this much information, Alice shut up like a clam. It didn't do to meddle with the occult. Next day she had a hiding from Father for spoiling his rose-bed. She'd picked a big bunch of his best blooms and wouldn't say what she'd done with them. She never said a word during the hiding, accepting Father's charge of 'wanton destruction' without a word in her own defence. Years later she told me that she'd laid the bunch of roses outside Ganny Wilson's door, whether to propitiate or thank her she didn't make clear.

Apart from contact with personalities like Ganny, we were conscious of fate in other ways. It affected our lives deeply, because we weren't cushioned off from chance by hazing security. We lived with the basic realities of sickness, death, unemployment; and we kept alive our awareness of fate in all sorts of old traditions, little reminders that there is always gaiety, humour and hope. We shared with the Ancient Britons an astonished delight at the recurrence of spring, and the season was thick with festivals: Tid, Mid, Miseray, Carlin, Palm, Pace-egg day.

There was the purely north-eastern anniversary of Carlin Sunday, when we ate the little grey peas, that had been steeping overnight, to celebrate the time the people of Tyneside had been saved from starvation by a cargo of carlins. On Palm Sunday the road to the tower was hanging with hazel catkins and pussy willow which we gathered to decorate our kitchens. Then on Easter Sunday we took our store of dyed eggs to bool them down the bank. The season of jarping was upon us and we'd all test for the hardest egg, then challenge all comers to a jarp, collecting with triumph all the eggs we'd cracked. Some of the lads made a business of jarping, and sold their damaged spoil at a nice profit.

Spring was the season of weddings, and all the bairns looked forward to the 'hoy-oot', when the bride's father threw coppers out of the car window. And an amazing number of births seemed to take place in the spring, so we had a grand time visiting the new babies, carrying with us a tiny good luck parcel for the mother. The ingredients varied, but they always included a packet of sugar, a box of matches and a skein of wool so that the baby would never lack nourishment, warmth or clothing.

A lot of the old customs were dying out, but first footing never will. In the last few minutes of the old year the ashes must be taken out so the fire burns clearly to welcome in the new year, then on the stroke of twelve a log of wood is placed on the fire and a tray prepared bearing a glass of home-made wine, a piece of spice loaf and a sixpence. This is for the first foot to cross your threshold, and if you're lucky it will belong to a dark stranger. A group of young miners used to roam about in the small hours of New Year's Day, knocking for entrance and bringing in with them a lump of coal and a sprig of greenery to bring luck throughout the year.

Every New Year's Eve Father would lift his glass of ginger wine and say, 'Here's hoping I'll see the next one in – that's if Greenlaw churchyard hasn't claimed me before the year's oot.' Then, wiping his moustache, he'd add, 'Ah well, if you live for ever, you've got to die sometime.'

This was the rhythm of life in Rainton. We never went far afield, but sometimes the world looked in on us. Once every year the football field became a fairground, and for an intoxicating fortnight the gipsies parked their caravans on the waste land next to the pitch. News would fly around and the bairns would yell, 'The shows is coming', to bring us all to our garden gates. We'd climb up dangerously and wave like mad at the big vans with their coloured floats, the horse-driven caravans where the gipsies lived and the chuntering steamroller which led the procession. We children were terrified of the dwarfs who worked underneath the big roundabouts, and when we visited the fairground we kept out of their way.

For miles around the lights of the fair beckoned. All the miners would take their sweethearts or children there and in the deafening din they'd ride on painted ponies, or swing dizzily up on the 'chairs' and shuggy-boats. The more sophisticated would gamble on the stalls but merely to be there amongst the steam and the sweat and the cranking and the loud crazy blare of the fairground music was enough for the bairns. Often there'd be fights, beer bottles would fly and lads would chase each other, shoving through the pressing crowd in Saturnalian ecstasy. There was danger and life and excitement when the shows came to Rainton.

Some of the older gipsy women would wander round the Black Rows, knocking on our back doors. It was unlucky to send them away, or you'd have a gipsy's curse on your head, so they'd be invited in, a coin would be spat on, and the gipsy would read the teacups, leaving even the most sceptical with an impression that 'there might be summat in it'.

The mystery has gone out of Rainton now. It has become a respectable Urban District Council, with fine street lighting and rows of council houses. Television aerials decorate most of the chimneys and there are pit-head baths at the amalgamated pit on the wide main road. It's unprogressive to feel nostalgic for the ill lit paths of the Black Rows, false romanticism to miss the sight of pitmen swaggering along, with their teeth glistening unnaturally white in their coal dusty faces. And nobody but a fool would wish the bad times back – when the men were out of work and the bairns ran about in rags with cracked old boots on their misshapen feet. But there was a life there once, a life that was lived in the strange half world between the miner's living tomb below and the gracious beauty of the wild countryside.

There was a tree that grew in Rainton, at the cross-roads through the bridge. You passed it on the way to the Charley pit, or if you were branching off to go to the next pit village of Linton. All the area round about was drab and ugly as if it wasn't worth the trouble to disguise its hideousness, because of the fog of grime that came down from the high pit chimney. Through the vomiting smoke you could see the slagheap behind and one of those sickening ponds that never run away and seem to be there for no reason at all. A few abandoned tubs lay about on their sides, forgotten, and one or two huts, given up as lost, still made a pretence at standing. It was a no-man's-land that stood inescapably at the gates of Rainton. At the roadside, with dramatic incongruity, the tree flourished.

It was always there – the first to celebrate spring in a frisson of urgent green shoots. In winter it stood stark and pure, a skeleton of beauty. In the autumn its leaves flaunted all the colours the black village of Rainton had been denied, and flung them triumphantly at our feet when a gust of wind threatened its splendour. I loved that tree. Every time I passed it I was teased by the incongruity of its setting, wondering whether it were more beautiful because of the contrast, or whether the quality was absolute.

It didn't take me long to realize that a mining village is a self-contained community or that the people who live in a place like Rainton are *different*. When the sales were on, Mother and Jane would take Alice and me into Newcastle as a special treat. Before we came home we went through the market and then sat in the railway station, watching the folks go by. They never failed to bewilder me. I'd stare in amazement at the painted faces and high-heeled shoes of the townies. I treated their appearance as a show put on for my benefit – nobody could go about by choice looking so daft and be normal. Although I enjoyed the excitement of the day out, I never felt secure away from Rainton. Puzzled about this, I once asked Father if he believed that travel broadened the mind.

'Grand thing, travel,' he said, folding his arms.

'I don't like anywhere else but Rainton,' I confessed.

'Well, you see, lass, that's because you don't know any other place,' he pointed out.

'Father, have you been to lots of places?'

Father puffed contentedly. 'A canny few,' he said after thought.

He tapped out the dottle of his pipe and put it away in the tin box on the mantelpiece. He laughed.

'A gipsy telt my mother once that I'd travel all over the world.' He paused, then repeated softly, 'All over the world.'

I was impressed. Gipsies surely knew.

'Aye,' he chuckled. 'That was nigh fifty years ago. Mind I've never been yon side of Gateshead yet – but you never know. I live in hopes.'

3. Perfect Friendship

LIKE all true pitmen, Father wanted no son of his to go down the pit. He never gave any reasons, except that it was no life for a lad, and he was hard to draw out about conditions down below. I think he was sadly disappointed that Fred didn't heed his advice, but couldn't wait to leave school and sign on at the colliery.

To me, as a child, his attitude was incomprehensible. Pits and pitmen had a magic for me that was tinged with awe. I loved to watch the pitmen coming back from work, with their pit dirt on them, lanterns on their caps, thumbs tucked into their string belts. I loved to hear the clip-clop of their heavy clogs striking clear on the pavement, and to witness the strange ritual when they greeted each other.

When it was fine in the holidays, Father would sometimes take me for a walk as far as the tower, then through the woods and back along the main road where the big pit stood. It was the regular Sunday morning walk in our district. Alice and I, dressed in our best, would join the regular procession of pitmen taking their bairns out for an airing along the tower road. The miners dropped their usual rough talk and spoke 'polite pitmatic' on their Sunday-morning stroll. They dressed in neat serge suits and sported their best caps and ostentatiously clean collars and ties. Nobody looked smarter than the miners on Sundays. Most of them sported a buttonhole culled from their own garden – a rosebud with a nice bit of fern usually – and all of them looked scrubbed with cleanliness.

During one school holiday, Father took me on this very walk. It was spring and there was the taste of Easter in the air, when the ceremony of jarping would usher in the beginning of the *real* year. One always quickened to life in the spring, and it was probably the seasonal tugging in his blood stream that caused Father to want my company on this occasion.

We started off, very gay. First we called in at 'the farm' which was between our house and the railway line. It wasn't really a proper farm, but old Mr. Nicholson – a bad-tempered old faggot – had three or four cows which he kept in a barn and a field to graze them in, up past the cross-roads. He also kept a few hens in a cree near the barn.

We didn't *call* on the farmer formally. We leaned over the gate leading to the outbuildings and breathed in the intoxicating mixture of manure and tar that Nicholson's land exuded. I concentrated on the hens scratching about for bits of yellow corn or boody, while Father examined the cows that Nicholson was rounding up.

'Owld Nick' wore a loose blue jacket and gaiters. He walked with a cautious heavy movement as if he distrusted the very earth that gave him his livelihood. He was notorious for his stinginess and his family lived in fear and trembling of him – even Percy, his huge surly son.

He pointedly ignored our presence until Father began to shake his head and sigh heavily, giving the cows a sad look. Nicholson slapped his heavy stick against the barn door and hopped in agitation.

'What's the matter with ye, man?' he squeaked fiercely. 'What are ye grunting and groaning for, eh?'

'Eh now, Bob,' drawled my father, goading him. 'Ye'll get had up if the inspector sees them coos.'

'Nowt the matter with the cows. What do you mean, inspector? What do you know about cows, or owt else for that matter?'

Father didn't reply. He stretched out a crooked finger towards one of the cows, whose bones stuck out alarmingly. Mr. Nicholson rattled his stick against the wire netting on the hen-coop, causing the birds to squawk and scatter.

'Aye,' he said impatiently. 'Thon cow's a bit off colour. Off its feed a bit. But there's nowt the matter with it really.'

'Thon coo's got T.B. if ever I saw one,' said Father with dramatic slowness. 'The flesh is dripping off its bones. You'll have to take thon to the vet.'

Mr. Nicholson was purple with rage. He danced round on the spot to give force to his utterance.

'Vet?' he squealed. 'No bleddy vet is going to see any bleddy cow of mine. Highway robbers, that's what they are. Vets? I've never heard the like. There's nowt at all the matter with that cow. It's just a bit off colour, that's all.'

Father smiled in an irritatingly superior manner.

'Well now, Bob,' he said in his politest voice, 'if you say so, you must know. You're the farmer, not me.'

'Aye,' growled Nicholson. 'Ye'd best remember that.'

We moved away from the gate and walked a few steps, then Father turned.

'All the same,' he added with deceptive mildness, 'I'd like to know what the inspector thinks of that coo yonder. It would be nice to have an *expert's* opinion.'

When we were out of earshot, Father chuckled.

'He's the meanest beggar on two legs,' he told me. 'But I frightened him. Old Nicholson fairly hates that inspector. I put the fear of God in him, I did.'

'Da,' I asked when he'd stopped laughing to draw breath. 'Has that cow got T.B.?'

'Oh, I shouldn't be surprised,' said Father. 'More likely he's not feeding it. Cannot bear to see the poor beasts eat, he cannot. Ye've got to give Nicholson a fright now and again, to keep him up to scratch.'

One thing was puzzling me.

'I don't think he was pleased, Father,' I said.

Father agreed forcibly.

'I don't think he liked us. I don't think he liked you saying that about his cows.'

'I'm damned sure he didn't,' agreed Father again. 'Do him good if somebody pulls him up about the way he neglects them animals. *I'm* not frightened of owld Bob Nicholson. He cannot do nowt to me.'

'But, Dad. If you don't like each other, what do we get our milk there for?'

Father became very proper and sedate.

'Well, hinny, we've always got our milk from Nicholsons. It wouldn't do to change. They're friends of the family.'

'Why can't we get our milk from the Stores – out of bottles? Then I wouldn't have to call at the farm with the can.'

I hated going to the farmhouse for milk, in case old Mr. Nicholson served me, but Father wasn't listening. He was gazing ahead. We had gone through the village, and turned down the road that led to the tower. The woods lay freshly green and budding on either side of us, a pale sun gave us its benison and pussy willows were dangling by the roadside.

'Aye,' said Father at last, taking in great gulps of air, 'I know more about coos than old Bob Nicholson ever did. Your father should have been a farmer, lass.'

I toyed with the idea. It never occurred to me to wonder what might have been, but the experience wasn't unpleasant.

'Would I have had to milk cows, Da?' I wanted to know.

'That you would, lass. Up at five o'clock in the morning. There's no sleeping in for farmers – except for folks like Bob Nicholson that doesn't know one end of a coo from the other.'

I didn't like the idea of milking cows. Their tails switched so, and they were always surrounded by fly-infested dung.

'I couldn't milk a cow,' I said with finality.

'Oh, you'd learn. Your mother could teach you.'

'Can she milk cows?'

'A finer milker than your mother never was born. Clever with it – neat and gentle as could be. Oh, yes, your mother could teach you how to milk cows, right enough.'

There seemed no escape. I tried another tack.

'Aren't you glad you were a pitman, Da?' At ten, I couldn't imagine a finer life.

'That I'm not,' he said decisively. 'If I had my time over again, I'd be a farmer – mak no mistake aboot that. Best life in the world.'

We were passing a field at the time and I turned my head at the sound of thundering hoofs. Several little black ponies, manes and tails flying, were careering around the field as though the devil were after them.

Father went up to the fence and called to them in a wonderfully coaxing voice, soft and caressing: 'Hey there. Howay there, lass. Come on.'

The ponies whinnied and went charging off, but Father was patient.

'Them's pit ponies, Mary,' he said gently. 'See thon one yonder, with that white mark on its brow? That one's just like the pony I had when I was marra with Charlie Westgarth. A white mark that puts you in mind of a snowflake.'

'Is it the same one?' I asked eagerly. 'Will it recognize you?'

Father chuckled, gazing over the fence with wonder in his face.

'No, hinny. That's a bonny long time ago. Charlie Westgarth's been deed a good many years now. Lost his life doon the pit like a canny few others. The best marra I ever had – by a long chalk.'

I watched the ponies with interest, trying to pick out the one with white on its brow, but they all looked alike to me.

'They're *wild*,' I cried. The ponies looked lost and bewildered, huddling together as if terrified of freedom.

'Aye,' said Father. 'When they fetch them above ground they go wild as soon as they smell the clover.'

'It's *cruel* to keep them down the pit in the dark,' I said vehemently. 'I think they're frightened of people when they come up. Look.'

I pointed to where they huddled in the far corner of the field.

'They're hiding from us. I'm going to climb over so they'll know I'm not going to hurt them.'

I put one foot on the wooden fence and was prepared to swing up, caution forgotten in a moment of pity, but Father stopped me.

'It's no use going over, Mary,' he explained. 'They can't see you, you know. They'd only be frightened.'

'Why can't they see me? Are they *blind*?' I laughed scornfully, but Father's answer was serious.

'They are at first, when they come up. They live under the ground, you know, where it's dark.'

'Oh *no*. Not blind!' I was horrified.

I opened my eyes as wide as I could. I could see white fluffs of cloud, bits of blue sky, the green of trees and hedges, black earth, the wooden fence and the moving mass of the ponies. Then I closed my eyes and all I could see was red streaked jaggedly with black. I tried to feel what it would be like to be a pit pony, closed up under the earth.

'Were you kind to your pony, Father?' I asked fiercely.

'Aye, I was very fond of Snowflake,' he replied. 'I used to take it a few blades of nice juicy grass and a clover or two in the summer. And mebbe a lump of sugar in the winter time. It always knew. Sometimes I'd make on I'd forgotten it, just for a bit carry on like, but Snowflake would give me a nudge with its heed and try to poke its nose into me pocket. *It* knew I never forgot it. A grand little pony, Snowflake. Dainty and neat on its feet. Could pull them heavy tubs as clever as owt and never put a foot wrong.'

'Did Snowflake *live* down below?'

At last I was going to find out something about that warm black land where the miners went.

'Aye, they all lived down there. Stables and everything – all white-washed. They had a lad looking after them, feeding them and brushing their coats and such like. Oh, they were well cared for, right enough.'

'Were all the pitmen kind to their ponies?'

'Most of them were, lass, but you always get the exception. Ted Dixon was a nasty-tempered beggar. He led his pony an awful life. One day it let fly with its back foot and caught him such a wallop that he vowed he'd kill it. He took a flying kick at the poor beast and it let out such a yell—'

One of the ponies whinnied and I looked at it startled, as if it were coming at me in vengeance.

'What happened?' I asked, horrified.

'Big Jim Taylor, the deppity, come running up and threatened that if Ted Dixon ever laid a finger on his pony again, he'd let him feel the weight of his fist. That settled it. Hand like a ham had Jim. Ted dursent say nowt after that.'

Justice had been done. I felt it was only right that the miners had their own laws in their own country. Deppity was boss.

'Charlie Westgarth and me had a good laugh over that, many a time. Aye, Charlie was the best marra in the world, bar none.'

I knew that the men worked in couples – they were marras in fact – and that they drew lots every fortnight to decide which seam they worked. A good seam was one where you could hew standing, but a bad seam was often waterlogged and low yielding, and had to be hewed under cramped conditions. Miners were paid on output, not on conditions. I wanted to know what a good marra was.

'Well, it's hard to say, lass,' said Father when I pressed him. 'He was a grand hewer, of course, but he was a cheerful fella to be with. He used to be always thinking up some new trick. I mind when I first went down the pit. I was just a bit nipper, you know, and my job was to keep the ventilator trapdoor open and shut so that the air could blow through the seams. Well, there was always a great big fire under the ventilator shaft and I had to pull this rope that worked the trapdoor, you see.

'Well, Charlie comes along and sees me sitting there freezing. There was a hell of a draught in front of the fire, cos all the heat went up the shaft, and I was shivering in front of that furnace. Charlie gives me a wink and quick as lightning he pulls an empty tub in front of the fire and turns it over on its end. Then we both sit inside the tub on our hunkers, warm as toast, out the way of the draughts.'

Father chuckled at the memory.

'Snug as could be we were,' he said. 'Mind you, there's nowt of that now. They've got these great fans now. All electrical. Conveyor belts into the bargain.'

His laugh was scornful.

'Call themselves pitmen? There's not a hewer among them I'd care to be marras with.' There was no stronger condemnation.

Thoughtfully we walked on until we came to the 'tower', so called because of its turrets. It was the lodge gates of the big 'hall' where the Carlton family had once lived. They had owned all the land round about at one time, but now the lodge gates were open and the public was allowed to walk down the drive which, with its arching trees meeting in fan-like delicacy, was a place of hushed wonder and delight. We sat down outside the lodge on the wooden seat thoughtfully provided by the local council, and Father got out his clay pipe.

Mother allowed him half an ounce of 'twist' baccy a fortnight, and he had to make it spin out. Soon he had his pipe going to his satisfaction and he sat contentedly puffing out rank clouds of thick blue smoke. When he'd finished he carefully scraped out the dottle and placed it inside a tin box that he kept in his waistcoat pocket.

'Nay, lass,' he said at length. 'The pits aren't what they were. And the pitmen isn't what they were neither.

'I mind when I was a young pitman. We had plenty of spirit in us in them days. There would be about six of us – Charlie Westgarth was among them. One night he was just coming yem from back shift. There was frost on the ground and a nice full moon – lovely. We came up from the pit and when we got out of the cage and set off to walk home, a matter of three miles or so, Charlie gets an idea.

' "Look lads," he says. "Take a smell of that."

'Well, we just stood there, the six of us and took a deep breath. After being choked-up down the pit, it was lovely – I can smell the smell of that night now.

' "Howay lads," says Charlie. "I'm not tired noo and I'm sure none of us is. Let's hadaway for a walk."

'Well the six of us sets off and walk as if we'd never just come off a hard shift. We were men, you see lass, ready for owt.

'It was funny to see all the lights out in the villages we went through

– and us singing at the tops of our voices. We made a rare noise, I can tell you. At the finish we landed up at a village about ten miles from home. It would be about four o'clock in the morning and we were ravenous. And we had a rare thirst on us, forby. So we stopped outside this pub.

' "Let's knock up the landlord," says Charlie.

'So we stood outside the door and threw stones up at the window until the landlord comes out.

' "What's up?" he says. "What do you want at this time of night?"

' "Something to eat and something to wash it down with," says Charlie, grinning.

'Well, the landlord cussed and swore and said he'd have the law on us, but Charlie took no notice.

' "We know our rights," he said. "Isn't that so, lads?"

' "Aye," we said, and we did.

' "By law," says Charlie, "ye must serve any traveller that wants it with meat and drink. Think yourself lucky we don't ask for a bed as well."

' "Travellers," said the landlord. "Ye're not fairly travellers. You've just come back from the pit."

' "We're travellers reet enough," we says, "and ye can like it or lump it."

'So there we were and there we stopped. We had a grand breakfast and we coaxed a sup o' beer out of the landlord. 'Cos when a pitman has a thirst on him, only beer can shift it. Well, when we'd finished we felt champion. Charlie calls the landlord ower and gives us all a big wink.

' "What do you do," he asks, "if you serve a meal to a party and that party cannot pay?"

'The landlord was laughing by now, 'cos he'd had a pint or two and was glad of the custom.

' "I kick the party's backside," he says.

' "Well," says Charlie, "take pay for six."

'And the six of us all bend over with our backsides up in the air.'

Father laughed so much at the memory that he started coughing, but I was horrified.

'Didn't you *pay*?' I asked.

'Not then,' said Father, recalling himself. 'Charlie called in the week after payday and settled the account.'

'What happened when you got home? Did you get wrong?'

'Oh, we got the hammer then, all right. But everybody could see the funny side.'

With a sigh at my obtuseness he got up from the seat and I handed him his wooden stick. His rheumatics were troubling him because the seat was damp, and we walked very slowly through the woods to the main road, pausing now and again so that Father could ease the cramp in his limbs.

The transition from country to pit village was very marked. Significantly, as we passed through the stile that led on to the main road, the sun went in and it began to rain for fairs. We stood for a moment at the stile, looking at the big pit chimney belching smoke. Some of the miners, just coming off a shift, were walking towards us with that characteristic slow swagger.

'What fettle there, Joe?' says one.

'Canny now, Bill,' replied Father. 'Hoo's theself?'

'Canna grumble.'

'Hoo's thoo gannin on there, Tommy?'

'Nobbut middling, Joe,' answers Tommy. 'The watter's bad in the seam I'm in.'

'Ah well.'

'Ah well.'

The time-honoured formula of pitmen greeting each other. I knew it by heart – the refrain had a tune and I could sing it. We collected in a little group to exchange the gossip, shouting over the pelting rain.

'Terrible thing aboot Nicholsons at the farm yonder,' volunteered Tommy.

'Oh?' said Father, eyes round with interest. 'Has there been some trouble?'

'Why aye, man. Did ye not hear tell what the inspector telt them?'

Hearing the sound of horse's hoofs we looked up and recognized the Nicholsons' milk cart being driven along by Percy, the farmer's eldest son, at a great pace.

'What cheer there, Percy?' yelled Father.

Percy's reply might have been a greeting or a snarl.

Father noticed that the lids of the big milk cans were missing.

'Letting the watter into the milk, Percy?' he grinned. 'That'll save you the trouble.'

Percy's face went brick-red and he whipped his horse along in a frenzy, splashing us all with mud.

Father shook himself and made a parody of a moue.

'Oh,' he said with false shame. 'That was tactless of me. No tact, that's Joe Craddock.'

I waited. One of the pitmen started to laugh.

'Thoo's reet there, Joe – more than you know,' he said. 'Like I was telling you – the inspector served a summons on old Mr. Nicholson this morning – for diluting his milk.'

A glance at Father's face showed me that the information wasn't news to him at all. Still, the families were close friends, I suppose, so they could take a joke.

4. Politics

A POLITICAL awareness is slower to develop than is generally supposed. A child accepts its environment, finding all the security it needs in the family unit. When this security is threatened, adaptation to change is often bewildering, especially for a child who can see that its parents are strengthened by a memory of security the child has never known.

My elder brothers and sisters had been born in better times and though they had lived through hardships, they were stronger to endure than I, who grew up in more turbulent times and whose strength was learned empirically by the speed of my adaptation to change. I was much the youngest – my arrival so late on the family scene could be judged a mistake or a pleasant surprise according to the point of view.

Sometimes Jane or Fred would exchange memories of the General Strike. Though they had lived through the bleak hungry days scratching the pit heaps for tiny lumps of coal, going to the woods to gather branches to burn in the empty grate, walking miles to the 'tick' shops, doing any odd jobs for a copper or two, learning to tighten their belts – nevertheless they had survived in a workless world. They were confident of survival because they knew that things had been otherwise and therefore could be otherwise again.

Their stories always had an element of adventure about them. They believed passionately in words like justice and freedom and human dignity, and they were fighting for their rights, against exploitation. Big issues were discussed among the miners at corner ends, solidarity was strong. Cold becomes a part of life and when things are desperate, neighbours come in handy. As soon as the belly is filled, hunger becomes a memory. So that for the elders of my family, the strike was an interlude – a bitter experience but, like a war, ultimately an event to be seen in perspective against the march of events.

To my parents, the strike period was at once an ending of a way of life, and the beginnings of defeat. It aged them both.

To me, who was a tiny child, it represented my norm – my own point of reference for my own experience. I was a quiet child, seeking in myself the calm that was denied me. Most of my infancy seemed to be spent in keeping out of the way – usually with the cat for confidant.

When the strike was settled, security returned to cloak the bitterness. The yellow windows of the Workmen's Club gleamed again and once more that distinctive swagger returned to the miners' gait. I reached the age of five, and it was my turn to go to the Infants' School.

I was unnaturally quiet on the day after my fifth birthday. My mother dressed me with care in Alice's old coat and brushed my hair until it stood on end with the friction. Then she took off her pinny and went into the middle room – hers and Father's bedroom. I heard the wardrobe door open and close and the rustle of paper wrappings.

I was overcome by the solemnity of the occasion. Mother never 'went out' unless it *was* an occasion. There was always far too much to do in the house. Now that Father was working again there were the pit clothes to beat and brush, the bait-tin to prepare and extra shopping to do in addition to the usual cleaning and scrubbing and mending. She had been up since five that morning to get Father out for first shift, and after the ritual of his departure she had left the dishes stacked in the sink and turned her attention to me – with the same single-mindedness with which she greeted every task.

I was kneeling on the floor cuddling the tabby cat, trying to quieten its angry cries but not relating them to my nervous grip, when I heard the middle room door open.

'Mary,' my mother cried, exasperated. 'Get up this minute. You'll get dirty lying about the floor like that. I haven't done the kitchen yet.'

I was yanked to my feet, crimson with shame, sniffing with shock and outrage, then I looked at my mother and my incipient tears stopped.

She was wearing her best coat (black, because you never knew) and a close-fitting black hat with artificial pansies spread all over it. A heavily spotted veil covered her face making her complexion look waxen and flawless. Her fine hooded eyes, sparkling with irritation, were like the blue eyes of a remote deity. A delightful smell of spring and freshness came from the perfumed spray of artificial violets pinned on her coat. I had never seen anyone so beautiful. I was bursting with pride and love, suddenly eager to go to the new school and show this lovely creature off.

Mother looked at my flushed face and stroked my cheek gently with her gloved hand.

'I doubt you're over-excited, Mary,' she said softly. 'You'd best calm down a bit. School's nothing to be frightened of.'

During the entire walk to school, which seemed endless but was really just past the railway bridge, I held my mother's hand and felt completely at one with her. When we reached the corrugated iron building, Mother took off my hat and coat, and hung them on a spare peg in the tiny porch, then took me into the baby teacher's class. I stared in exposed horror at fifty pairs of eyes while Mother talked to the teacher, then I stepped quickly behind the protective black coat and tried to swallow, but my throat was dry.

I peeped out and saw a blackboard with a clock face drawn on it. Underneath the easel was a rocking-horse with a moth-eaten mane. With obsessive solemnity I focused hard on the brass tacks which held the mane loosely to the painted body. Then my mother's hand, warm through the glove, gave mine a quick squeeze and she was gone.

The teacher put her cold bare hand on my back and gently impelled me towards the back row, where she told me to sit and gave me a sand tray and some bright beads to play with. Then I was left alone, trying to take in this enormous room which bulged with children, trying to adjust to a wider society, composed of my peers.

The class was chanting 'A for apple, B for boy' and as soon as I found my voice I joined in. At last I was enjoying the adventure – at last I belonged to an entity. I thrilled to the experience and yearned to belong fully, to be accepted as a member of the group. I succeeded so well in adjusting myself to my first experience of practical politics that when, a few moments later, I saw my mother's face through the glass partition as she stood talking to the headmistress, it appeared to me as the face of a stranger. When she raised her black gloved hand and waved to me my face stiffened in a smile of embarrassment and I cast a sly glance at my class-mates to see if they'd noticed. Mothers were incongruous at school. I was more conscious of the small hole in the palm of the black cotton glove than I was of Mother's attempt to convey wordless reassurance through the glass partition.

I had a wonderful time in the Infants, which was a true democracy. We weren't big enough to hurt each other and we settled everything by an unconscious instinct of majority approval. We were all cells in a corporate body, and we had a double existence, our real life as a part of the group and a shadowy life at home with grown-ups. We were remarkably incurious about each others' backgrounds but hyper-sensitive to flaws of character.

I remember feeling pleased one morning in the playground. A new arrival had been brought to our classroom – a little girl who screamed when her mother tried to leave her. When the teacher allowed the child to ride on the rocking-horse in an attempt to placate her, a wordless flicker shot through the class. We disapproved of softness. At morning playtime none of us spoke to the little girl. I was pleased – not to inflict pain – but to be identified with the group wish. *I* hadn't cried – I had been spartan. My reward had been not a ride on the rocking-horse but spontaneous acceptance into the community. As a member, I had no sympathy for a little girl who tried to bring the emotional blackmail of the adult world into our society.

My school life made so many demands on my loyalty that it was much more real to me than life at home. When the pit closed down and Father went on the dole, I hardly cared. I had playmates in the Black Rows who wanted me not because I loaned toys and balls, but because I could always invent new games. I was consulted even by our recognized leader, who by flattery turned my potential rivalry into allegiance.

At the age of eight, I started at the 'Big Girls' School', another little pond that to me seemed so big that it dwarfed me to the size of a minnow. Then a shattering thing happened. My two worlds clashed, or rather my home life suddenly swelled in importance and broke into my child's world. I made the discovery that no one exists in isolation. It mattered who you were, or rather who your parents were. I discovered with acute shame that we were on the Means Test. The State had invaded our privacy. Father couldn't get a job. No pit manager would take on a man over fifty, especially when he had the rheumatics so badly. Times were hard.

However, at the price of our liberty, the State would see that we didn't starve. Jane was pupil-teaching so the bulk of our family income was derived from Fred, who naturally resented working down the pit for a measly bit of pocket money. It wasn't fair to ask him to support our parents and three bairns at school. He frequently pointed this out until Mother rounded on him one day and asked him what pocket money she ever had.

'Every penny you bring into the house,' she hissed, 'and that's precious few – goes on food. There's nothing left over.'

Of course the situation was impossible. But the solution, when it came, was more like a disaster. The State struck us where we lived – not in our pockets, but in our pride. Take away self-respect and a corroding shame enters that eats away at the heart of a person.

I arrived home late from school one evening, rosy-cheeked and ravenous, anxious only to snatch a piece of bread, then dash out to play. I cannoned into Jane, at the back door.

'Where've you been?' she asked sharply.

I mumbled that I'd been kept in.

'What for?' The professional touch.

I stood still, mutinously silent.

'Fighting, by the look of you,' she snapped. 'Get into the scullery and wash your face, then come into the kitchen. Quietly. We've got a visitor.'

Her eyes were reddened as if she'd been recently crying. Awed, I did as she told me, then we went into the kitchen together.

The whole family was there, looking like an illustration out of *Sleeping Beauty*, fixed eternally in significant attitudes. Their faces had a peeled look of blankness as if all personality had been washed out of them. I was seeing them as the stranger saw them. Father was in his usual chair by the fire, sitting crouched so that I could only see his wispy hair. Ted and Alice were sitting neatly together on the couch while Fred, the eldest, had a seat at the table opposite the stranger. Mother was sitting alone, straight-backed on a kitchen chair that she'd set against the wall, leaving the discussion in the hands of the men-folk. Her eyebrows were raised and she gazed unblinkingly at the stranger, who beckoned me forward.

I was used to school inspectors and instantly placed the stranger as one of 'them' – a term which included doctors, clergymen and any official who wielded authority. He had spread out his papers on our table and referred to one of them now.

'So you are the youngest,' he stated. 'What's your name?'

It was a question all adults asked.

'Mary Craddock,' I rattled off. 'Where do you come from?' was usually next and my lips started to form the answer, 'Black Rows'. Recently I had discovered that 78 Carlton Place was my real address and that the wonderful black rose I imagined as giving our estate its name was merely a contemptuous term of reference for our ugly rows of black wooden houses.

'And you go to Rainton Girls' School,' the stranger continued. 'What class are you in?'

'Miss Nixon's class,' I answered promptly.

'Standard one,' said my sister quickly.

'How old are you?'

'Nine next birthday,' then, remembering that this was an official, 'Eight and three-quarters.'

Father raised his head and winked at me. He looked very shabby in his old trousers and boots, and his muffler seemed like an affront to this spruce civil servant. I cast an eye at his overcoat carefully folded on a chair and saw that it was lined with gleaming satin.

There was an uncomfortable silence while the stranger's pen scratched on the form. I sensed hostility in the air and looked quickly at Fred, noticing how big and clumsy his hands looked as they lay on the plush tablecloth. Fred wanted to say something – do something violent – but he was holding himself in check.

The toff was finished with me. He put down the pen and leaned back. The chair creaked and the sound was ominous in the heavy silence. I crept quietly towards my mother, feeling instinctively that she was being got at.

'Well,' said the stranger. 'That's the situation. What are you going to do?'

He looked straight at Fred who felt at a disadvantage because he still had his pit dirt on him and smelt of warm earth and darkness. The grime on his face made the whites of his eyes shine and gave a red glow to his lips so that when he spoke intensely he looked so comical that I wanted to giggle.

'*I* cannot do nowt,' said Fred angrily. He glared at Father who sat with slumped shoulders, not even looking at the breadwinner.

'We'll manage somehow,' said Father mildly. 'There's worse losses at sea.'

Mother reinforced his attitude with a nod, but Jane was an emancipated young woman, impatient of the stoicism of Mother's generation.

'We'll have to face facts, Father,' she said. 'Fred and I'll have to leave home. There's no alternative.'

Horror shocked through me. This was the worst thing that had ever happened to the family. The vague dread of disruption was now to become a reality. The family would split up, and our security would crumble.

I flung myself on my mother, who stroked my head absently, giving no comfort. It was all that man's fault. Impotent anger possessed me. What right had he to walk into our kitchen and tell us what to do? Why was anybody taking any notice of him? I stared with loathing at his lined overcoat and patent leather shoes, trying to understand what the change would mean.

Fred cleared his throat with familiar vigour. He must have been straining as I was against the clerk's authority, and felt the need for self-assertion. Up till now he'd relied on the strength of his hands to earn him his keep and a position of privilege in the family. He'd been contemptuous of Father ever since we'd gone on the dole. When Fred came back from work, everything must stop until he'd had his tub wash in front of the fire. He had Mother running round like a scalded cat fetching hot water or scrubbing brushes or towels and she had to answer his roar of 'Wash my back' whatever else she might be doing. The best that was in the house was offered to Fred and his word was law.

Although I shared his opinion of the stranger, even at that moment I felt a shiver of joy at the sight of his frustrated red face and big raw hands lying so helpless on the table. All of us watched him.

'Aye,' he said thickly. 'I'll leave home. I'll do more than clear out of the house – I'll leave the bloody country. It's done nowt for me.'

I could feel my mother stiffen. She was more outraged at his outburst in front of the Means Test man than she was at the thought of his desertion.

'That's enough of that, Fred,' she said sharply.

I looked at my father. Written on his face was a helpless despair that I'd never seen before. He'd reached rock bottom. Jane went over to him and put her hand on his shoulder, then faced the clerk.

'I'll get digs in Allanvale near the school,' she said curtly. 'So you can see for yourself that everything's fixed up.'

The Means Test man looked uncomfortable.

'I'm only doing my job,' he said wearily. 'I don't make the regulations.'

Jane's expression showed him what she thought of his job and he turned away from her to make a note on the form. The pen scratched once more in silence. You could have stirred the gloom with a ladle.

'I've put down that you have no means of support,' he said at last. 'And three dependants.'

Father nodded bitterly. 'That's about it,' he agreed.

'That means that you'll be eligible for public assistance,' the man went on, 'on the understanding that if anybody helped you, your allowance would be cut.'

'Aye, we understand all that, reet enough,' said Father. 'You've made it quite plain.'

'If you were to resume employment,' the man continued, ignoring Fred's snort of disbelief, 'then you must inform us immediately.'

When he'd gone, Jane went across to Mother.

'I'll come home every week-end, Mother,' she said urgently. '*And* I'll pay for my keep.'

She looked at Fred who was still sitting at the table.

'A fine son *you've* turned out to be,' she said witheringly. 'The sooner you're gone the better. We'll be a lot better off without you.'

Mother shook her head. 'Fred's done his bit,' she said, 'but it wasn't enough.'

But Fred's face was closed against anger and fairness. He was on his own now – a man for himself. And we were on the Means Test.

That was my second big lesson in practical politics. I saw how economic pressure could change a family. I saw my father gradually accepting his role of useless incumbent. I saw the struggle against shame and worry leave their mark on my mother. I saw Jane receive the deference that had been Fred's. One's value seemed to have a direct relationship to money.

Jane's clandestine visits at week-ends had been fun at first. They had united the family against interference. Once she'd had to hide in the far room, owing to the unexpected arrival of the 'queer fella', Dad's term for the Means Test man. Later she began to resent the secrecy, then the visits. After Fred got married, my parents were always surreptitiously watching Jane for signs of romantic interest, warning her of the dangers of throwing herself away on an undesirable.

The atmosphere at home deteriorated. Father spent long hours in the club with his more fortunate mates, trading conviviality for a gill of beer. When he came home he was surly with shame. Mother never said anything, but her eyebrows went up and her lips tightened. She had far too much pride to brawl. The neighbours regarded her as stand-offish because she didn't waste hours gossiping with them or bemoaning her fate. There was another reason for her aloofness. She was starting to go deaf.

All this had an effect on me, too. I no longer felt sure of myself with my playmates. I never asked any children to the house, preferring the companionship of Alice and Ted who didn't prod me with questions. When I called on my school friends at their homes, their mothers would ask me in and question me about our circumstances. When I admitted how bad things were, I would be given a sweet. I felt a passionate loyalty towards my mother and when I betrayed this to earn the sweet or apple I never received at home, I felt guilty and sick, so that when the sweet turned sour in my mouth or the apple proved wormy, I was glad.

I was in the scholarship class at the Girls' School when the incident occurred that was to crystallize my sense of class consciousness. Though most of us came from working-class backgrounds, there was a sprinkling of girls from richer homes, distinguished by their plumpness and cared-for clothes. More remarkable than their neatness was the fact that their clothes fitted them because they had been bought only for them, not with an eye for the future generation. One girl, Nancy Bell, was the teacher's pet, always being held up as an example of neatness. She was always ready, with a complacent smile, to display her flawless exercise books, or to give advice on brushing hair or cleaning teeth. I disliked her vaguely for her smugness though I accepted toffees from her until one day she called me greedy because I never offered toffees back. The reason was simple. I never had any, and her reminding me of the fact caused me to dislike her personally.

One afternoon the teacher asked us all to stand on our seats while she inspected our shoes. At that time I boasted two pairs of shoes – an old pair of boots that 'took in' and a cheap but beloved pair of ankle-strap slippers which I was allowed to wear at school at odd times. I was so convinced that this was a slipper day that I didn't even look at my feet while the teacher inspected them. I disliked the feel of a teacher so close and when she raised her head her glasses were too near my face.

'Come and see me after school, Mary,' she said, then went on to inspect the others. All the girls looked at me and I made a pantomime out of the genuine astonishment I felt, until I glanced down and discovered that I was wearing my old boots. Teacher must be keeping me in after school to give me a lesson on how to polish shoes.

After school, however, the teacher asked me what size shoes I wore. I told her, then she went to the cupboard and came back with a brown paper parcel.

'Take these home with you,' she told me. 'It's a pair of shoes that Nancy has grown out of, so Mrs. Bell very kindly sent them along for one of the girls. I'm sure your mother will be glad of them in times like these.'

She held out the parcel but I couldn't bring myself to take it. All I could see was Nancy Bell's smug face and I went crimson with fury.

'I don't need any shoes, thank you, miss,' I got out. 'I have another pair at home – patent leather ones.'

I drew in a vast breath for the telling shot.

'Mother says these are good enough for *school*,' then I turned my back on the bewildered woman and ran all the way home, arriving there breathless.

Father cocked an eye at me.

'What's the matter with you, lass? You look fair wun up.'

I snarled an answer and flounced over to disturb the cat. Stroking the soft fur and burying my head into its stomach to feel the purr, I felt my anger dissolving into self-pity. Jerky little sobs were forced from my body. The whole story came out. Somehow I turned the resentment against my father.

'It's all *your* fault. Why don't you get me another pair of shoes then they won't all *laugh* at me.' I was shouting through the sobs.

Father didn't reply. The next moment I received a sharp slap across the face.

'Don't speak to your father like that,' said Mother. 'I won't have it.'

She'd come in from the scullery and caught the tail end of it.

'Leave the lass alone, Jennie,' said Father wearily. 'It's understandable.'

This wasn't enough forgiveness for me. I wanted my mother to tell me that she approved of my attitude. Patiently Father repeated the story for her benefit, and I watched her face as she sorted it out.

'Well,' she said at last, 'you could have done with the shoes, but I suppose you did what you thought best. Only – don't come whining to me or your father to buy you things in future, when you go throwing back people's kindness in their faces.'

With this equivocal reply I had to be content, but I was beginning to think that perhaps beggars *couldn't* be choosers. Was there also to be a price-ticket on pride? Or was Mother's apparent compromise caused not by the ignominy of having accepted public charity, but by something more personal? She was trying to come to terms with the isolation that deafness brought with it. Perhaps this personal struggle for security was making her disinterested in things like pride or self-respect. In any case, my mind was made up. *I* would not be patronized. My political consciousness was hardening.

When I won a scholarship to the Grammar School, and entered another little pond as a minnow, I took the opportunity to cloak myself in another personality. I became something of a court jester privileged to express myself as an outsider, free from the powerful pressure of conformity. I now wanted to examine the pattern which I had once wanted to fit into so eagerly.

At fifteen I heard of communism. I loved the slogans, the little pills of wisdom went down my gullet painlessly – 'The best for the most' – 'From each according to his ability, to each according to his need.' I wondered if schoolchildren counted as workers of the world.

I took to going alone for long country walks, to think of ways to put the world to rights, without realizing that the world lay at my own back door.

One afternoon I was walking back through Birley on my way home from school, when I saw my father. His old muffler and cloth cap, his boots and frayed trousers suddenly appealed to me as the badge of the worker. I overtook him and surprised him by walking the rest of the way with him. He could only walk slowly on account of his rheumatism, but I didn't mind. I felt a glow of sympathy for this oppressed member of the proletariat. We walked in silence for a while, companionable on my part, constrained on my father's.

He asked me how I was getting on at school, but my replies were perfunctory.

'Dad,' I said at last. 'Have you ever heard of communism?'

I was prepared to explain it.

Father stopped and opened his mouth wide, rolling his eyes in exaggerated astonishment.

'Is that what they teach you at school?' he asked. 'That rubbish?'

I was instantly aflame with revolutionary zeal.

'Rubbish? It's the only hope of the working class. How can you ever get anywhere when you're exploited by capitalists? Look at Russia – the workers' state.'

'Don't talk out of the back of your neck, child,' my father said impatiently.

'What have you got against them?' I asked. I was appalled by his attitude, but then he was old. It was youth which must carry the burden, I convinced myself, feeling young.

'Communists? Aye, we've got them here. Look – do you know what I think of them? Riff-raff, that's what they are. Corner enders. Them as wouldn't work if they could. On the look-out for something for nowt. Them's communists.'

He spat, squelching the gobbet with his foot.

This was simply prejudice. I spoke fervently of the evils of capitalism, trying to fire him with my vision. He heard me out, looking at me tiredly.

'Aye,' he said at length. 'We all know what's wrong. We all know what we'd like to see. But there's two words I'd like to put to you.'

He cocked his head up slyly at me. 'But – how?' he said slowly.

What could be done with him? I gave him up, but I felt uneasy. Then I saw my chance. We were walking past a street of slums sardonically called 'Mount Pleasant', and I grabbed my father's arm.

'Look at it,' I said. 'That's what capitalism did for you.'

Father and I surveyed in silence the grim ugly street that had been put up to house the pitmen. It was incredibly ugly, drab with gaping windows and rotting doorways propping up slatterns in sack aprons and curling-pins. Inside one could glimpse disorder born of despair. I saw it as a failure of the System. Father had a different view. He was looking at the slatterns and their filthy little kids.

'Aye,' he agreed. 'It's a very bad area this. It's a terrible thing to see the way people let themselves go when they've lost their self-respect.'

Involuntarily he straightened his shoulders as we walked past 'Mount Pleasant'. We walked on a little way, then Father stopped to search in his pockets for a box of matches. He opened the box with care, then took out a match and handed it to me.

'See if you can break that,' he said.

Impatiently I snapped it in two. Without a word he handed me the box, with 'Now try to break that.'

Foolishly I did try, but of course it was impossible. I said so, suspecting a trick.

'No trick at all lass,' he said. 'Ye've seen for yourself how easy it is to break one thing, but when there's a bunch, it's well nigh impossible.'

He tapped the matchbox with a horny forefinger. 'That's why I'm a union man, do you see? You seem fond of catch-phrases. Well, here's another one for you – Unity is Strength. And that's a good 'un, because it's true.'

I thought this over as we resumed our walk. Presently we stopped again. At the corner end we came across a strange sight. An earnest young woman was standing on a soap-box talking rapidly in a harsh voice. She made a bright splash of colour with her red coat and college scarf, and was being watched attentively by an old man and a little boy busy picking his nose.

Father and I stopped to see what she had to say. I recognized all the opinions I had been expressing to my father, dressed up in finer-sounding words. After a while I wasn't listening to the words. I was looking at her stout leather brogues with little tassels on, and the fur gloves on her gesticulating hands. From across the gulf set up by her clothes, her fine words sounded patronizing.

I smiled at Father and he winked back at me, then he walked quietly over to the student and tapped her on the shoulder. She paused in her harangue and blinked at my father, obviously wondering if he was a convert. In an area like this she must have supposed she'd sounded like a prophet. But Father – and now I – knew different.

'Gan home, hinny,' he said kindly. 'Gan home.'

And she meekly did as she was told.

We walked home together, Father and I, sharing a tacit assumption that communists knew nowt about people.

I started to tell Father how the union movement had begun, and he gave me his courteous attention the rest of the way.

5. The Neighbours

RAINTON was created by the pits. It is a huddle of streets dotted with pitheads and it lies at the bottom of Rainton bank because that's where the coal is. The countryside round about is wild and beautiful and nearby there are one or two real country villages with traces of Roman occupation. But Rainton is neither old nor beautiful. As a shrewd visitor once said, 'There's this to be said about it. It's easy to get away from.'

When you'd said that, however, you'd said everything. Apart from the wide main roads that lead to Newcastle and Wearmouth, there is no distinction in Rainton. In local parlance it's called 'the last place God made'. Dominated by the huge pit chimney which scatters pit dust round the whole area, Rainton on a wet day is like a primaeval swamp. The village has five pubs, one church and a Co-op which runs the length of the main street. For the rest, the village consists of street after street of jerry-built terrace houses. For years our family lived off the main road in the Black Rows, which had been hastily put up when the pits first started to draw miners to the area.

They were old wooden houses of the bungalow type, consisting usually of three rooms. The front door opened from the garden straight into the kitchen, a big room with one wall taken up entirely by the old-fashioned range. The other two rooms were bedrooms. Outside the

49

back door we had a lean-to scullery, where we kept the poss-tub and mangle. The coal-house and lavatory were situated about forty yards distance from the back door, standing at either side of the open ash-pit which was cleaned out at intervals by an itinerant midden man.

In front of the house stretched the miner's glory – his garden. I've never met a miner yet who wasn't skilled at growing things. It's as if they want to restore to the earth they've violated for coal some of the richness they've taken. Even the gardens at the Aged Miners' homes bloom like a restitution.

At the bottom of our garden, by the gate, Father had built two crees. One had been claimed by Ted as his working shed and the other was a hen-cree. As we lived in the corner house at the end of the estate, we had some extra land, so apart from the utilitarian stretches of vegetables – potatoes, carrots, lettuce and cabbages, we had a fine rose-bed and a magnificent row of sweet peas. The edge of the path was lined with up-ended bricks, behind which bloomed a border of small flowers – marigolds, pansies, love-in-the-mist and sweet-scented stocks. Pride of place was claimed by the leek bed, next to the compost heap. Leeks were Father's speciality and they were grown not to eat, but to show.

Mother insisted on having a rockery just beside the front door. She, usually so upright a woman, had no scruples about taking slips from tiny plants that grew in the public park and transplanting them in her rockery. Nasturtiums grew there in profusion and she was always on the look-out to protect her daffodils from the thrusting mimulus. Down beside the gate – Father's showpiece – was a glorious array of phlox, gladiola, sweet-william and poppies. On Mother's insistence he had trained rambler roses to grow right over the fence.

A privet hedge separated our garden from that of our neighbours', the Morrisons. Beside the hedge grew two fine bushes – black currants in Morrison's garden, red currants in ours, but each bush sent our fruit-bearing sprays into the other's garden.

It seems a pity that the families could not have followed the generous example of their fruit bushes. But as long as I can remember, relations between the two families was one of intermittent but concealed warfare.

Old Jimmy Morrison was a cantankerous old man. Normally he had a face as long as a fiddle, but every Saturday night he went to the pub and came back as merry as a lark. His whole personality was reversed – he was as genial and generous as a robin. There was something birdlike about his Saturday metamorphosis, but for seven days and six nights in the week he was a spiteful, close-fisted old beggar.

As a family we kept ourselves to ourselves. We didn't borrow or exchange gossip over the back-yard wall, so we were regarded as stuck-up by the neighbours. All except Father, of course, who always had a word for everybody. But then he delighted in the intricacies of human relationships. He knew more about the history of every family in Rainton than any man living.

Mother lived vicariously through him. She rarely went over the doorstep, but Father brought the world to her. Every night we could hear Father's voice through the thin wall which divided the middle from the far room. He would lie with his face close to Mother's ear and patiently he would recount all the events of the day. Even when she was *stone* deaf, Father could always make her hear. Mother wasn't avidly curious about people's lives, but Father's racy comments shocked and delighted her. Half of the fun of Father's stories was a hearty disregard for the truth. Everything was sacrificed to make a story dramatic, but his tales were so pleasant in the telling that we didn't care if they weren't true. Reality is what you make it.

Father's imagination played around the Morrisons. He was convinced that old Jimmy Morrison was a miser.

'He never stands a round at the club,' he'd insist. 'Stands to reason he's got a canny bit put away. He's ower mean to give a beggar a kind look.'

And every time old Jimmy went into his garden, Father would watch him from behind the lace curtains in the kitchen. For he was convinced that a suspicious old cove like Jimmy wouldn't trust his fortune in the house where Nellie could get at it, but would bury it secretly in the garden.

The Morrisons' garden was undoubtedly neglected, but I thought it was because he was too mean to pay for seeds and too lazy to spend time and energy in digging – a labour for which he wouldn't receive wages. It never occurred to either Father or me that old Jimmy was suspicious of us. But when I was helping Father in the garden, I could see the curtains twitch in Morrison's window. Father interpreted these signs of counter-spying as proof that he was on the right lines. For sheer devilment he played on the old man's suspicions.

We had at the time a little black cat called Nipper, whose intelligence was well above average. How he did it I don't know, but Father trained Nipper, when he let it out to do its business, to ignore our garden and slip through the hedge into Morrison's. There it would dig a great hole in no time at all and we'd all watch behind the curtains to see old Jimmy

Morrison come running down his path, cursing the cat and throwing at it anything within reach. Nipper was much too shrewd to be caught and she'd nip back through the fence, climb on top of the cree and sit there washing her paws as unconcerned as you like, knowing that she was out of reach.

The insolence of the cat delighted Father, who would reward Nipper with a bit of meat. He had a wonderful way with cats. When she was a kitten, Father taught Nipper all kinds of tricks and trained her to recognize the fact that when he sharpened the big gully, it was a prelude to cutting the joint. The little black kitten would come flying in, tail hoisted, and clamber up Father's trousers on to his shoulder. Then Father would give it little bits of gristle which it ate purring from his cap.

When Nipper grew up, Father regretted his training. He daren't open the knife drawer without the cat's hearing him and come flying up to his shoulder – from the sideboard, the window-sill, even from floor level, and the weight of its body arching in feline ecstasy would cause Father to stagger round the floor from the impact, cursing the cat at the top of his voice.

He never objected when she dug holes in Morrison's garden though.

'He'd like to morder that cat,' he would chuckle when old Jimmy chased Nipper back to our garden and stamped back the earth she'd scratched up. 'Aye, our Nipper's got him fairly worried. He'll be up at midnight the neet, you mark my words, shifting the tin box with all his money in. Nipper, lass, here's a bit of meat for you. You're getting warmer, Nipper. Ye'll be red hot next time.'

Father seemed to spend most of his gardening time leaning over the wooden gate passing the time of day with his cronies. One or other would be bound to stop and inspect the treasured bed of leeks near the bottom of the garden.

'Them's fine leeks, Joe,' he would shout.

'Aye,' Father would agree heavily.

Silently they would inspect the leek bed.

'Are ye putting them up for show?'

Every year all local growers would show the best of their produce competitively at the club. There was money to be won, but more important, envy. Prestige in a pit village depended not on feats of strength or size of pay packet, but on growing skill.

'Aye, I am that,' Father would reply solemnly.

'Thoo should be all reet with them uns.'

Father would walk slowly over to the leek bed and inspect them critically.

'Thon's a fine leek,' his crony would point out. Father would sigh doubtfully.

'If she doesn't borst,' he'd admit cautiously. 'Look here,' and he'd lift up a flag of the leek tenderly in his crooked old hands and point out a tiny crack at the bottom.

He knew his leeks better than he knew his children. He'd confuse our names when he called us. I was 'Jennie – Alice – Mary' to Father.

Old Jimmy Morrison hated the idea that Father could grow better leeks than he. For Jimmy came of a leek-growing family, and his brother used to come every year from a village ten miles away to fetch Jimmy seed from prize leeks. Father grew his own seed and always did better than Jimmy at shows.

He used to tease the poor old man. I watched Father from the bedroom window early one morning. He crept cautiously out of the front door, carrying a pail, stopping every few yards to look round furtively. Then with his back to the houses he bent down over his precious leek-bed and sprinkled something from the pail over the soil round his leeks. That done, he crept back silently into the house.

I slipped into the kitchen and saw that he'd collapsed into his armchair convulsed with laughter. He opened his eyes and winked at me.

'He saw me,' he gasped. 'I knew he'd be watching. Old eagle eye was looking out. I'll give him something to think about, spying on me.'

I tried to get some sense out of him.

'What did you put into the leek bed?' I asked.

But Father shook his head. He wasn't telling.

'Ye know nowt about it,' he admonished me. 'And if anybody asks you, say you don't know.' That was easy enough.

'I won't tell anybody,' I agreed. 'Only tell *me*.' Father closed up like a clam.

'Blessed are those that expect nothing,' he replied, 'for they shall not be disappointed.'

I think that was the only bit of the Bible he knew.

What Father was up to with his leeks, nobody knew. Then one day Father surprised us all by putting on his Sunday clothes in the middle of the week.

'Where are you off to, Joe?' asked Mother.

'Out,' said Father. 'Mary – Alice, me stick.'

I handed him his plain wooden stick but he brushed it aside.

'Not that – me other one. On top of the press.'

So I reached for the bone-handled cane with filigree steelwork round the tip.

'That's more like it. Well, I'm off.'

We weren't the only ones watching him go down the path, smart as a toff, handling his stick elegantly. A few minutes later old Jimmy Morrison stumbled off down *his* path, putting his muffler on as he went. There was no doubt about it – he was following Father.

'Spying on Joe, that's what he's doing,' said Mother tight-lipped, twitching back the curtain, then dropping it quickly as Jimmy reached the gate. 'Well,' she went on, pushing me back from the window, '*we* can mind our *own* business.'

Mother's Olympian calm wouldn't do for me. I grabbed my coat and was out of the door haring after my father before she could check me. I overtook him at the corner end where he'd paused to have a bit crack with the amateur politicians. A group of them were squatting on their haunches and you could pick out the unemployed by their defeated look. All of them had on caps and mufflers and they eyed Father's best suit with mock envy. One of them smote his forehead with the flat of his hand and gazed at the closed doors of the pub with dawning comprehension.

'Eh, man, it must be Sunday,' he said, bemused. 'That's why it's all shut up.'

During the laughter that greeted this sally, Father tweaked his buttonhole, waiting.

'Where's thoo off to, Joe? Come into a fortune? Ye look as if you wouldn't call the King your uncle.'

Father basked in the general admiration, then enlightened them in polite pitmatic.

'If anybody asks,' he said sedately, 'I'm going to pay a call. On an old friend.'

'Who's that then? Johnny Walker?'

'It's a bonny long time since I had the pleasure of *his* company,' retorted Father. 'Not since eggs were twelve a dozen. No, I'm going to call on Sidney Green.'

I edged round the group and hovered near Father.

'Shame on you, Joe,' shouted one. 'Gannin alang to see a swearing atheist, and you a good-living chapel man.'

Under cover of the appreciative jeers, I tugged Father's coat. The men caught sight of me and I hid behind Father to escape their focused attention.

'Why, here's the bairn been sent to stop him. Where are you off to, hinny? Alang to the Rechabites to sign the pledge?'

Scarlet with shyness, I was on the point of tears when Father rescued me from the men's pelting laughter, by accepting my presence as if it were the most natural thing in the world.

'Mary's coming alang to see I'm not contaminated,' he answered. 'She keeps me on the straight and narrow,' and he put his big hand over mine, holding it there until we were out of sight of the corner enders.

I was sniffing by then, but Father spoke gently.

'Divent take any notice, hinny. They're only having a bit carry on. There's no harm in any one of them.'

I'd feared a rebuke for trespassing on male territory but, emboldened by his attitude, I told Father that Jimmy Morrison was following him and that I'd come to warn him.

'You did reet,' he said with a nod and I was happy. 'You can come alang with me for company.'

Father never deigned to look behind, but I kept a close watch. When we reached the herbalist's shop I kept guard outside while Father went in on business. I hopped up and down on the stone flag outside the shop window, then I saw Mr. Morrison shuffling along over the crossings. Immediately I dashed inside and tugged Father's coat, indicating our neighbour's proximity with nods and grimaces.

To show he grasped the danger, Father closed his eye in a wink. He was in a jovial mood with the herbalist and I felt lightheaded as I breathed in the laughter and good fellowship and the lovely mixed smells of the herbs. We gave Mr. Morrison plenty of time to walk past before we emerged from the shop. I carried the paper bag, taking excessive care with it as Father had bade me. Old Mr. Morrison was nowhere in sight. Father and I surveyed the streets with care then grinned at each other.

'Aye, we've fairly given him the slip. Noo we'll had away off and pay a call on Sidney Green. And if owld Jimmy Morrison hears tell of that, much good it'll do him.'

As we walked past the neat little streets of stone houses that flanked the road out of Rainton, something puzzled me.

'Da. What's a swearing aytheest?'

Father considered my question gravely, before he said: 'Funny things, atheists. Never goes to church or owt. Don't hold with God, you see, or owt like that.'

I digested this information carefully. 'Is that why they swear?'

I knew that swearing was sinful. Father chuckled a little.

'Aye, I suppose so. Mind – it doesn't mean that anybody that lets drop a cuss or two when they're vexed is an atheist.'

That was my first lesson in logic. I nodded, relieved that Father wasn't an atheist.

'Is Sidney Green one?'

'Aye, he is that. Always has been. Pleasant-natured chap at that,' he added in wonder, 'but he'll argue blue murder with chapel folks.'

He paused to get his bearings, then he led me up a narrow alley to the back streets.

'He married a chapel girl,' he explained. 'Sarah Wilson. Been dead this many a year. Turned him against religion you see, 'cos he had to bring up a big family by himself. Now they've all gone off and left him, bar one, Martha. She's the eldest daughter, and she had to stop at home to look after him.'

He unlatched the gate of Mr. Green's back-yard and thumped on the scullery door with his stick. Although dressed for a formal visit, he wouldn't dream of going to the front door, as that wouldn't have been friendly.

While we waited outside, Father said softly: 'Grand fella, Sidney Green. Tremenjus capacity for beer. Aye he was a gay lad in his time. Known for his wildness. But for all that, a very strict man with his family, a great believer in the strap.'

After a long pause the door was grudgingly opened and Martha Green peered out at us, the eldest daughter who had sacrificed her youth to her father, and instead of getting married had acted as foster-mother to her own brothers and sisters.

'What fettle?' asked Father briskly. 'Just happened to be passing this way and I thowt I'd like a bit crack with Sidney. Tell him it's Joe Craddock to see him.'

Martha, a rangy woman with the look of an unripened bitter fruit, nipped her lips together and didn't budge.

'He's failing,' she threw at us. 'Cannot last much longer. Doctor says he's not to be bothered.'

Father grinned sociably and she relented enough to open the door a crack further, contenting herself with, 'Dinna be long then.'

'Just a few minutes,' agreed Father with false sincerity, then we were admitted into the living-room. A bed had been made up in the corner and on it lay an emaciated figure. His white hair lay on his skull in fluffs as if it had no roots but had alighted like feathers from the air. Over his closed eyes the lids looked like purple bruises. Father caught in his breath in involuntary pity, shocked at the change in his friend.

The eyes opened and took in my father. Then Sidney Green's face underwent a startling transformation. Blood seemed to flow visibly into the wasted cheeks, the mouth took on colour and widened into the ghost of a cheeky grin.

'Hoo's theself, Sidney?'

'Eh – why it's Joe Craddock.'

He reared up on his pillow, clutching the knitted coverlet in his excitement.

'Sit yourself down, man. And tell that lass o' mine to fetch a cup of tea apiece.' He groped for a pleasantry, then brought out, 'Nowt stronger, Joe, I'm afraid.'

Father eased the old man on to his pillow and told me to slip out and tell Martha about the tea. I went into the stone-flagged kitchen where Martha was busy scrubbing the deal table.

'Well, what is it noo?' she snapped, brushing back a lank strip of hair that had escaped the iron curling pins. Timidly I gave the message at which she snorted with impatience.

'Tea is it? Just like him – wants to be waited on hand and foot. Here – set them cups out.'

Silently I did as I was told, keeping out of her way as much as possible. Martha exuded a bitter force that filled the tiny kitchen and nipped in the bud any attempts at frivolous conversation. I was glad to get back to the living-room, despite the queer smell from the old man in the bed.

The air was crackling with: 'Do ye mind this?' and 'Do ye mind that?' and old Mr. Green's eyes were as bright as a child's. From the talk, he must have been a proper devil when he was young.

'Aye,' said Father at last, 'you always spoke your mind, Sidney, no matter who it was, or what it cost you.'

It may have been my fancy, but the old man seemed to plump out. At any rate his voice was stronger when he insisted: 'And I haven't changed a bit, Joe. And don't intend to neither.'

Martha brought in the tea and an aura of scrubbed silence, but she gave her father a sharp bold glance before she shut the door with a significant click.

'Proper bitch, thon,' was his comment.

'Nay, Sidney,' protested Father. 'She's been a good daughter to you. How would you have managed without her?'

Mr. Green waved aside this truth with a frail claw.

'She's taken after her mother,' he hissed. 'A proper devil for chapel is Martha. Cannot get enough of it. She's always after me to turn. Do you know what she did when I took a turn for the worse? Fetched a bloody preacher to see me.'

The old voice quavered in self-pity.

'And me a swearing atheist. It's not good enough,' he said with impotent petulance.

'Well, noo, I did hear that you were thinking about making your peace with the chapel folks again,' put in Father.

The effect of these words on the old man was magical.

He shouted: 'Is that what they're saying at the club? I've lived an atheist and I'll die an atheist. I won't have them chapel folks taking an unfair advantage of me.'

He'd obviously intended his daughter to hear, because we could hear her banging about in the kitchen in reply.

'And you can tell them this in the club,' he added. Father nodded seriously, listening. 'I've lost the use of me limbs, but there's nowt wrong with me heed. And I'm not dead yet, not by a long chalk.'

'Ye'll have to stop alive to see that chapel folks don't bury you,' agreed Father. 'Well, we'll have to be off.'

'Tell them I've changed me mind about dying,' the old man added. 'Or mebbe I'll be along one of these days and tell them meself.'

Just before we left Sidney showed Father something that he'd hidden under the bedclothes. 'That's for an emergency,' he told him with a wheezy chuckle that turned into a paroxysm of coughing.

Martha turned us out with an angry flounce. Outside, the damp air was good to breathe. We took the short cut home, up by the old line, past the pit heaps and the allotments.

'Da. What was Mr. Green showing you?'

'Nowt.'

I pressed him, guessing: 'A bottle of beer?' but he shook his head.

'He said it was for an emergency,' I insisted. 'What was it?'

Father turned to me conspiratorially. 'It was a leather strap,' he told me. 'He fetched all his children up by it and he's holding on to it at the end. If it *is* the end. Sidney's not ready to go yet, to my way of thinking.'

He shook his head and his eyes held awed admiration.

'Hasn't changed a bit,' he said. 'Sidney Green, the swearing atheist. Ruled his bairns with a rod of iron. Aye, he's cheated the undertaker again by the looks of it.'

When we got back Father told me to give to my mother the brown paper bag I'd carried all the way from the herbalists. I ran off to the scullery where Mother was washing the pantry shelves, and handed her the package excitedly.

'Open it, Ma,' I yelled. 'I want to see what it is.'

Mother pushed me away and opened the bag, which contained yellow powder. So this was the stuff Father put on his leeks! Mother's casual attitude to the packet annoyed me, after the careful treatment I'd given it.

'That'll come in handy,' she said, popping the packet into the boot box which served as our medicine chest, 'but I don't see why he had to make a special journey for a bit sulphur. Now you'll have to go to the shops for a tin of treacle. One's no good without the other.'

I was furious at Father's treachery. I had no objection to his bluffing old Jimmy Morrison, but to fool me, who was his ally! Back in the kitchen, I found Father contentedly puffing his pipe as he watched our neighbour limping up the path next door.

'I'll teach him to follow me,' he said with satisfaction. 'We've given him the slip, lass, good and proper.'

Although our victory seemed pointless, I forgot my disappointment at the sight of Father's pleasure and winked back conspiratorially.

The next step in the war of the leeks was taken by old Nellie Morrison, Jimmy's wife. Warning us of her intended visit by banging with the coal rake on her side of the chimney wall, she came into the kitchen the following morning, holding a cracked cup in her hands.

'Ye wouldn't have a bit bicarb to spare, would you, Mrs. Craddock?' she said in her piercing voice, then when Mother hurried off to the pantry, she stood in front of the fire, warming her backside.

Nellie Morrison was a big skinny woman with stringy grey hair pulled back from her pasty brow, and a permanent drop at the end of her nose. She affected a false air of geniality but her mouth shut like a trap after every bit of gush that fell out of it. Her sharp button eyes missed nothing and they soon fixed on me where I sat under the table hugging the cat.

'Not at school, missy?' she rapped.

Her daughter, Flossie, who played the piano at the mission, was 'filling in' by being a caretaker at the Big Girls' school, while she waited for something better to turn up. As Father pointed out, however, she'd been waiting for seven years now. No doubt Flossie had reported my absence.

'I've got whooping-cough,' I hiccuped. 'Doctor says I've to stop off.'

'Oh,' she said with a nasty grin. 'That's it, this time, is it? I thought your shoes must have taken in again.'

I blushed as she cackled heartlessly. Mother had let me stop off school one wet day because my boots were worn from the uppers, and she couldn't see her way to getting them mended. Rather than let me catch my death of cold, she'd allowed me to play truant but the School Board man, warned no doubt by Flossie, had called and learnt the shameful truth. Trust Mrs. Morrison to remember.

'Where's your father?' she asked suddenly.

'Out.'

'Not along at Sidney Green's again, is he?' she asked with sharp suspicion.

I shrugged. She wouldn't get any information out of me.

A huge smile appeared on her face, the falseness of which could be detected a mile away.

'Do you help your father in the garden, Mary?' she cooed. 'That's a good lass.'

I whooped a cough at her for answer.

She waddled over to the window and inspected the garden, arms akimbo.

'Them's grand leeks he's got there,' she went on in her treacly voice. 'What does he put on them, Mary, to make them grow so fast? Does he tell his little gardener? Or is it a secret?'

She smiled with effortful archness at me.

'Stuff,' I answered, immune to flattery.

'What stuff?' she rapped, hoping to surprise me, but I remained silent.

'Aw, he wouldn't tell a bairn like you,' she said carelessly, losing interest in me and walking back to the fireside.

My pride was stung. 'I *do* know,' I shouted, hiccuping furiously. 'But he said I wasn't to tell.'

Her eyes narrowed and she gave her huge head such a nod that I thought it would fall off.

'I *thowt* as much,' she muttered slowly. 'He's been getting stuff from somewhere to make his leeks grow.'

Mother came back just then with the bicarb. Nellie snatched the cup off her, muttering something about two being able to play at that game, then was off through the back door without even a thank you.

'Well!' said Mother arching her brows. 'Some folks.'

She went off pointedly to wash her hands, then came back to put the kettle on.

'Your father'll have something to say about this,' she said briskly. 'She didn't get anything out of you, did she?'

I shook my head. I didn't think so. All the same I felt uncomfortable when Father came back with the shopping.

'Nellie's been in,' said Mother, emptying the bag. 'You've just missed her.'

'Oh? What did she want?' Father pricked up his ears.

'Bicarb, she *said*,' emphasized Mother meaningly. 'She tried to get something out of the bairn here.'

I told my father everything that had happened, expecting a rebuff for giving secrets away, but he heard me out with a quiet smile.

'That's reet, lass,' he said mildly. 'Never tell nobody nowt. That's the best way.'

I felt relieved, but a bit uncomfortable still.

'Da,' I said, struggling. 'I didn't *tell* her. But I think she guesses.'

'Let her guess away,' he replied airily. 'That's nowt to worry aboot. Ye have to have brains to guess with.'

That cheered me, until I remembered something.

'She said two could play at that game,' I offered.

'Did she now?' Father opened his eyes wide. 'Did Nellie say that? The old lass isn't as green as she's cabbage looking.'

But more than that he wouldn't say.

A day or two later, the doctor allowed me to go back to school, and for the next few weeks of term I was more interested in playing outside than in helping Father with the garden. This was the time of year for the game called 'Give a holla' and the memory of it quickens my blood even now. We all gathered at 'base' round an old tin bucket punched with holes. We lit a fire inside the bucket and fed it with sticks and coal dust wrapped in blue sugar bags. Then the two leaders elected teams, leaving the odd man out in charge of base where he supervised the fire. Sometimes he had helpers who would roast spuds for us over the home-made brazier.

Next, the two leaders would produce the turnips they'd pinched from somebody's garden and carefully hollow out the middle. Inside we'd put a lighted tallow end, then we'd toss up for 'hunters' and 'hunted', and the game would start. To the slow count of a hundred, the 'hunted', with doused lanterns, would quickly make themselves scarce, then the hunt was on. Sometimes the hunters would wander for miles looking for the escaping team, and when they were giving up, they'd yell 'Give a holla'.

From far in the distance, like an echo, would come the reply, 'Holla-holla'. Quickening with the scent, the hunters would cup hands over mouths and the refrain would wing from them – 'Shine the muggie – shine the muggie'. For answer the flickering light of the other team's turnip lantern would gleam in the distance for a tantalizing moment, and the game would be on again. The sport held magic for all of us, and we'd go indoors with the memory of it lighting our night faces, to the alien world of home.

During the holidays, all the miners were getting ready for the big autumn show at the club. Father wanted my help with the leeks. As I was the youngest, I protested that I had other things to do, but I was flattered at Father's picking me out to help him, so I relented.

'I cannot handle them properly with my hands, hinny,' he said, trying to spread them out. 'Leeks needs very careful handling. You don't want to damage the flags, you know. They're femmer things, is leeks.'

So I handled them with exaggerated care, slipping the tape measure round the thick white stems which had been carefully washed with milk.

'Them's fine leeks, Jennie,' Father pointed out to my mother. 'Nothing coarse about them leeks. A different class altogether from his next door.'

Mother looked judicial, not wanting Father to build up his hopes too much.

'Morrison's leeks look big enough to me,' she said doubtfully.

'Nowt at all of the sort.' Father was hopping about in his agitation. 'They *all* look big from here. Look at my bed if it's leeks you want to see.'

Nevertheless he was worried. Old Jimmy Morrison had been going about for the last week or so with something approaching a smile on his wizened little face. He'd said nothing to Father, merely grunting in exchange for greeting, and huddling away off if he thought he was going to be tricked into conversation. One day he rattled Father badly by leaning over the garden gate, watching Father closely as he tended his leeks, then, after spitting in the direction of the compost heap, turning away with contempt. For once Father was speechless and didn't even attempt to detain his neighbour.

'Da,' I said, plucking his cardigan sleeve. 'I saw Flossie in the Stores today. And do you know who she was talking to?'

Father shook his head, his eyes on the leeks I was handling on the scullery table.

'Mr. Willson, the herbalist.'

'Niver the world!'

'True enough. They were getting on like a house on fire. You know what I think?'

He didn't seem interested, but I told him anyway.

'I think old Mr. Morrison has been getting the same stuff for his leeks that you got.'

Father looked startled but covered it by saying: 'Be canny how you're putting them leeks in the basket, lass,' then, as I complied, he added, 'we'll see the neet.'

That evening all the locals who were showing at the club toffed themselves up and went off with laden baskets. When the produce was judged, only the showers and judges were present. The following night the show was open to the public and we'd all go along and look at the exhibits bearing their proud placards.

We all wished Father luck when he set off and waited impatiently for his return.

'Whatever happens,' he told us, his hand on the sneck, 'I've got every confidence in the judge.'

The evening dragged and we watched out for him anxiously.

'Here's Father now,' cried Alice at last and sure enough we heard his step on the flagstone. He stood beaming on the threshold, then went up to Mother.

'We've won, Jennie,' he said, putting his lips up to her ear.

Mother was delighted. We all crowded round, congratulating him.

'Where was Jimmy Morrison?' we chorused.

'Thon fella? He was nowhere,' and Father set off laughing and coughing beerily.

'A funny thing happened,' he went on. 'When Jimmy got his leeks to the show, they looked a fair treat. But as soon as the judge put a finger on them, they borst wide open. The judge took one look at

Jimmy and said one word – Disqualified. He could see the leeks had been forced, you see.'

He shook his head in disapproval.

'Anybody could have told him that it doesn't do to meddle with leeks. They're like bairns, is leeks, you have to look after them.'

He started to shake with laughter again.

'Ye should have seen old Jimmy Morrison's face,' he said gleefully. 'He gave me such a filthy look, but I wasn't to blame. If only he'd asked for advice – but then Jimmy Morrison never would own up to his ignorance.'

He shook his head at the defection of Jimmy.

Before I went to bed I wanted something straightened out. I got Father on his own and helped him off with his boots.

'Father,' I said firmly. 'Tell me honestly. Did you feed your leeks with some stuff you got from the herbalist?'

'Whatever makes you think I'd do a thing like that?' asked Father round-eyed.

'Well – what was it I saw you putting on the leek-bed? You remember – I caught you early one morning. What was in the pail?'

Father closed one of his eyes. 'Nowt,' he said.

'Nothing?' I echoed. 'But what was the idea?'

'I just wanted old Jimmy Morrison to think I was stealing a march on him,' he replied. 'Some folks'll believe owt. Silly old beggar.'

'But what did you go to the herbalist's for? Just to go on fooling him?'

Father filled his pipe and didn't reply until it was drawing to his satisfaction.

'Partly that,' he conceded. 'And partly to find out whether it was true that his brother was going to judge the leeks at our show.'

He puffed out a great cloud of smoke.

'He comes from Avelstan, his brother,' he told me with satisfaction. 'I know the family weel.'

6. The Depression

SOME events are too big to be taken in. Faced with the gigantic experience of a war or a depression, people tend to focus on small personal memories, as if the huge catastrophe had been distilled into something the size of a keepsake which has the power to touch off the larger issues. So that when people talk of the 'Depression' I am reminded of the workhouse smell of Greenlaw Hospital.

Though Father was out of work, he was a great union man. In fact, he was treasurer of the local Miners' Union for our area. People used to come to our house with their green union cards if they couldn't go to the office, and Father would put their coppers into a big leather bag and fill in the card with a great flourish.

In the early thirties, times were hard. There was a good deal of unemployment in the area and the corner ends were crowded with silent groups of miners squatting together for comfort, out of the way of their wives' scolding tongues.

Conditions in the Jackie pit were very bad. The accident rate was high because the machinery hadn't been renewed owing to insufficient capital. Men were constantly being laid off, and those who were working had to face waterlogged seams. Father had worked the Jackie for a spell and it was where Fred worked, so he took a personal interest in it.

I remember the day that Fred, my strapping great brother, came home with fourteen shillings in his fortnightly pay packet.

'The bloody Jackie pit's finished,' he said bitterly. 'There's more slate than coal coming out of them seams.'

Father shook his head. 'It's been a grand pit in its time, Fred lad. And there's still plenty of coal doon there, if the pit was handled right.'

'Handled right?' echoed Fred. 'It's downright scandalous in some of them seams. Some of the pit props is so rotten they'll cave in on top of us one of these days.'

So it wasn't altogether a surprise when we learnt that the Jackie pit-men were going on strike for better conditions and a living wage.

Union delegates from all over the area met to consider the claim, and they decided that the strike was unofficial. They realized that the pit's life was nearing its end anyway, and when unemployment figures in the whole county were so high, the majority of delegates considered that the Jackie pit employees were lucky to be working at all.

There was a big meeting of the local miners in Rainton to discuss the union decision. They took over the Store hall which was usually let for wedding parties and concerts. Father and Fred both attended the meeting and they came home flushed and confident.

'Unanimous decision,' said Fred with satisfaction. 'We're all going to stay out, unions or no unions. 'We'll see if the bloody owners can get on without us.'

But Father's face was worried. As a union delegate he knew how powerless the strikers would be without union backing, much as he sympathized with the cause. The owners could sit tight and live like camels off the hump of their capital, whereas the miners were nearly at rock bottom, fortified only by their pride.

Countless meetings were held. Everybody clubbed together. Neighbours acted in a neighbourly manner, normal factions forgotten. There was an exhilarating spirit of togetherness in the community, especially at the beginning. The strike, with its appeal to human dignity, had sounded out of us a chord of harmony.

We had a bit put by in the Stores – it went. Mother put on her thinking cap and drew on her store of country knowledge, contriving to keep something in the broth pan, even in the worst times. But lines appeared on her thinning face and her feet lost their confident sprightliness. It was a bad time in Rainton.

Then one Sunday the sun shone, so Mother called for Alice and me.

'The blackberries should be just about ripe now,' she said briskly. 'Get yourselves a basket each and come along with me.'

The three of us togged ourselves up like gipsies in our oldest things. Mother put on Father's shabby old mackintosh which flapped round her ankles, while Alice and I donned our hated tartan skirts and jumpers from the rag bag. We set off with our baskets and walked along the tower road, suddenly gay.

Then instead of turning off through the woods, we went straight on past the cross-roads along a new untravelled road. On either side of us fields stretched out and the smell of clover was in our nostrils. We were all a bit intoxicated by the adventure and sense of freedom. Rainton was a good place to be out of. We shed its gloom with every step we took along Mother's route.

Suddenly Mother called a halt.

'It's about here,' she said, then her sharp eyes picked out a gap in the hedge.

We scrambled through and walked lightly across the fields, over a stile and into a meadow. There before us lay bramble bushes in profusion, laden with big juicy fruit. Not a soul was in sight. We regarded Mother as a magician who had conjured up wealth for our benefit.

'I told you I knew a good place,' she said, enjoying our pleasure. 'I used to come here as a girl.'

We tackled the bushes with a will, but eventually our energy slackened. We were tired with the fresh air and the long walk. Our hands, even through our mittens, were bleeding and scratched from the bramble thorns. Above all we were ravenous and dry with thirst.

'Here,' said Mother when the baskets were half filled. 'Rest your legs a minute.'

We found a hummock and lay back luxuriously, watching the clouds stain the blue like lumps of clotted milk.

Mother dived into her raincoat pocket and produced a packet of little mints, hoarded heaven knows how long. We sucked the fluff off them rapturously and stretched our legs out on the grass. Mother had a gay, almost reckless air. She was reminded of her youth, a rare thing with her.

She told us of the time she'd cheeked the squire who had reproved her for walking past his drive with her dogs unleashed.

'Get them damned dogs out of my way,' he'd yelled at her.

'They're not damned dogs, sir,' Mother had replied. 'And I'll thank you not to swear at me.'

Even now, forty years later, she recollected that show of spirit with pride. It was an unheard-of thing to speak back to the gentry in her young days.

Alice and I exchanged a glance of tolerant amusement, then dusted ourselves and went on with the picking. Suddenly our peace was gone. There had been a timeless, spaceless element about our meadow. We felt it had belonged to us because we were there. Now we saw a farmer in the next field, leaning over his fence and shaking his fist at us.

'Get off them bushes,' he yelled. 'You're trespassing. Be off with you.'

Mother couldn't distinguish the words and thought he was shouting a greeting.

'Lovely day,' she shouted back and put a big juicy bramble in her mouth.

The farmer's face took on a shade of purple. Alice and I put our belonging together, then tugged Mother's sleeve.

'We're tired now,' we told her. 'Don't you think we'd better be getting back before it gets dark?'

With her faith in the civility of country people unbroken, Mother led us back through the ploughed fields on to the main road. We'd picked nearly two full baskets amongst us and Mother was happy calculating the amount of jam she'd be able to get out of the fruit.

Immediately we got home, Mother bustled about making preparation. We climbed up to the top of the press for the big jam pan, scoured it carefully, then started to wash the fruit. Mother produced a packet of sugar that she'd hoarded against an emergency and carefully stirred it into the strained juice. The hob on which the jam pan rested had been turned back so that the jam could have the benefit of the fire. The sweet sticky smell from the pan spread through the house like a benison.

Father and I were keeping an eye on the pan while Alice tried to get a thorn out of Mother's hand. They'd gone into the scullery where the light was better. The scene is always recalled for me in slow motion, perhaps because of my lethargic state after all my exertion, perhaps in contrast to the events that followed.

For suddenly, without warning, the jam bubbled over and started spurting into the fire.

Father's mouth dropped open and he just stared. I, too, seemed incapable of doing anything except watch the trickles bubbling hysterically on the bars of the grate.

Then Father let out a yell that was a rallying cry for action. He hobbled over to the pan and tried to lift it but didn't have the strength in his arms.

Stumbling over the cat, he made for the scullery, yelling as he went: 'Alice – Jennie – Mary, fetch summat. Look slippy. Fetch a pan or summat.'

I dashed ahead of him for the tin pot, but with a crazy logic, stopped to wash it out first. I reached the fireside in time to see Father making ineffectual swooping motions with a cup. The absurdity of our actions made me shriek with laughter.

'Stop that cackling, Mary,' said Father testily. 'Thoo's not a hyena.'

'Here,' I shrieked, offering the tin pot. 'Mind the jam. It's scalding.'

'Use your gumption,' he yelled back. 'Don't get ower near.'

I clung on to him helplessly, urging: 'Let it boil,' not wanting him to get too near in case he had an accident.

Then the pair of us were swept aside. Mother found the handle and with one swoop of her powerful arms lifted the red-hot pan from the hob and set it safely down on the hearth. Action always came quicker to her than thought. Father and I looked at one another with our inadequate pots dangling from our fingers, and grinned sheepishly.

'Wonderful head in a crisis, your mother,' muttered Father.

Alice was bending over Mother and the two of them were making little cries which had seemed to be gasps of laughter. Suddenly we realized that Mother wasn't huddling over in laughter, but in pain. She'd burnt her arm with the scalding jam and Alice was trying to see the extent of the damage.

'Here, Mary,' said Father, suddenly efficient. 'Run into the pantry and fetch a handful of flour. That's a bad burn she's got. Alice – get hold of a bandage. We'll have to keep the air off that arm.'

Mother insisted that she'd be all right.

'Stop fussing,' she kept saying. 'I cannot abide a fuss.'

Had she been in her normal health nothing would have happened, but she was run down with worry and improper feeding, so the arm began to swell painfully. Although she managed to handle the bulk of her work, she had to admit that the arm wasn't healing properly. The flesh round the thorn spelk was festering.

It was useless telling Mother to go to the doctor's, so Father took the law into his own hands. He made a special trip to the doctor's (we were panel patients) and asked him to look in while doing his rounds the following day.

'He's an impitent beggar, thon,' he commented bitterly on his return, 'but I telt him he *had* to come. So he'll look in tomorrow.'

When the doctor called, Mother's arm was bulbous and discoloured. Dr. Mason examined it closely, then looked round the kitchen.

'I'll need a clean basin and some boiling water,' he said curtly, busy with his bag. He pointed to the bread poultice we'd put on to draw the wound. 'You can throw that thing into the fire.'

Then he approached Mother, who was sitting meekly on a straight-backed chair. 'Just turn your head to one side,' he told her.

I could see her bite blood with the pain of it as he lanced the swelling. Dr. Mason had no time for a bedside manner with panel patients.

'Basin,' he shouted, and Alice held it while the bad blood dripped out.

The doctor's professional manner intimidated me. None of us dared say a word, except Father.

'Has it turned septic?' he asked, worried.

'No, it should be all right,' answered Mason as if every word cost money. 'Tell her to rest the arm and come along to the surgery for bandaging. It should heal up in a day or two.'

He glanced at his watch, then shut his bag with a click. His time was precious.

'Take it easy,' he said to his patient, then a moment later he was off in his car.

Mother's face was white, so we made her a cup of tea and put her feet up on the hassock.

'I've never liked Dr. Mason,' she said faintly. 'Always in too much of a rush. I didn't see him clean that knife.'

'Ye should have spoke out at the time, Jennie,' agreed Father fussily. 'I wish I'd noticed. They think they can get away with owt when you're on the panel. It's different if you live up past the bridge.'

Mother's arm still gave her pain and when Jane came home at the week-end she went straight along to the surgery to play war with the doctor. She must have put the fear of God into him because when he came back to see Mother he sent straight for an ambulance to take her to Greenlaw Hospital.

All the neighbours collected outside our gate when the ambulance drew up, and they watched in gloomy silence as the stretcher-bearers carried Mother out.

'I doubt we've seen the last of Mrs. Craddock,' said one old wife as the doors slammed behind her, and I stooped instinctively to clutch a stone to throw at her, but I hadn't the heart to throw it.

The house wasn't the same without Mother. Trixie, the tabby cat, used to sit inside the lace curtains and stare out of the window as if she knew that something was wrong. She began to fret.

One night the cat took a long look at each of us in turn, then miaowed to be let out for the night. Alice went to open the door, but I felt a sudden panic.

'Don't go out, Trixie,' I said, clutching it, but Father wouldn't let it stay indoors.

The next morning Trixie didn't come back. I searched the garden and the long rows of earth streets in the Black Rows. I even went through the bridge and up to the park, but Trixie never came back. I mourned its loss with extravagant grief, but it was more than Trixie I mourned.

The day arrived when Father took me to Greenlaw Hospital to visit Mother. She lay in a ward with her hair, braided in unaccustomed plaits, lying neatly on the gleaming white coverlet. Her hair was greyer but her face looked rested. The skin shone with more than cleanliness, it had that stretched look that sick people get.

Her hands lay stretched out over the bedcover. One arm was huge with splints and bandages, making the other look tiny. Her free hand looked white and delicate under the frilly calico sleeve. Normally Mother's hands were rough and calloused with all their heavy work.

While Father talked to her, Mother's huge bright eyes rested on me. I couldn't find anything to say, she seemed so strange, so I wandered round the ward looking at the other strangers. I went on tiptoe so as not to disturb the sepulchral silence. It seemed fitting that the windows had bars across, because the patients were prisoners of their sick bodies. On my wanderings I was particularly taken with the sight of three huge gall-stones in a glass jar. I made my way back to Mother's bed. I had something to tell her.

'That woman's got gall-stones,' I whispered, pointing. 'They're in a glass jam jar with her name on.'

I waited for Mother to accept my offering, frowning at her sternly. She smiled and touched my sleeve with that alien white hand, nodding at me for answer.

'Take good care of your father, Mary,' she said softly, and I gulped, suddenly overwhelmed with loss. She hadn't understood. We'd made no contact.

'Did you tell her about Trixie?' I muttered thickly to Father, who shook his head. We got up. Visiting time was over and nothing had been accomplished. Mother's eyes followed us all the way to the ward doors. I could still feel them as we walked back home up Greenlaw Hill, then over the fields.

'Da,' I said when we'd paused to rest at the top of the big bank, 'I didn't like that place.'

We sat down on the council seat, looking back at the tree-lined road we'd travelled, down at the little village of Greenlaw nestling below. It was a very quiet village, but there was something wrong about that quietness. Greenlaw should have exuded a feeling of peace, stemming from the ancient church that dominated the square, but it wasn't peace. It was an empty silence, a hollowness at the centre of the village, which I sensed. Father nodded.

'Nor me neither,' he said heavily. 'Nor your mother for that matter.'

He looked at me closely, then decided to explain.

'You see, hinny,' he said, 'Greenlaw Hospital used to be the work-house. It's run by the same people.'

My heart leapt. Mother in the workhouse? That was the unspoken dread in everybody's life. Father noticed my agitation and explained.

'Folks like us cannot afford hospitals or owt like that, hinny. Think how much it would cost for all they're doing for your mother yonder.'

He was trying to cheer me up but his voice was bleak. I thought of the harsh clean smell of the ward and the grim barred windows.

'Is it charity, Father?' I asked.

'It's for poor folks,' he said quickly. 'What can't afford anything else. Do you mind them cottages we passed, beyond the church there?'

I nodded. There had been a date on them – 1886.

'Them's for old folks that's got nobody to look after them,' he explained.

'Like the workhouse?'

'Aye, just like the workhouse.'

'Why is everything so quiet at Greenlaw, Da?'

It was the quiet of defeat that I'd sensed in the village, the unnatural quiet of those with no help. I felt it but couldn't explain why it made me uneasy. I only knew that I didn't like the thought of Mother in that place.

'Do they look after her in there?' I wondered.

'Oh aye, they do their jobs.'

I remembered Mother's unhappy eyes watching us as we walked out of the ward.

'She'd be better off at home,' I insisted.

Not that there was much comfort at home, with the strike still on. Fred's temper grew sourer every day and Alice was wearing herself out trying to cope with the housework after school.

Sometimes Ted would take me along to the pitheaps and show me how to pick out the bits of real coal. If you went early in the morning you stood a better chance, because later the big boys used to come in groups and throw stones at you if you were on their territory.

Old Tom Johnson, who lived three doors away from us, was having a hard time. He was fond of his pint, and used to frequent Burdon's pub at the cross-roads. The landlord was sympathetic, but business-like. He allowed the strikers to chalk up an account on the slate, to be settled come payday.

Apparently Tom had attended one of the strikers' meetings, after which, flushed with success, he presented himself at Burdon's bar.

'I'll have a pint, Bill,' he told the landlord.

For answer, Mr. Burdon jerked a thumb at Tom's slate, which was fuller than anybody else's.

'Oh, that's all reet,' said Tom expansively. 'We've just had a meeting in the Store Hall. Unanimous decision. All debts is weshed oot.'

He got his pint. Burdon knew when he was beaten in a battle of wits.

That episode seemed to mark the turn of the tide. The graph had reached rock bottom, and now it started to rise, shakily at first, but definitely. The strike was settled and once more the miners' wives started to shake the pit-clothes outside the back door. Conditions would definitely be improved and a face-saving compromise was reached about wages. Nobody was really satisfied with the outcome, but the men's pride had been preserved. You can't dictate terms to miners, and you can't push them about, because they have a bed-rock dignity which cannot be violated.

Fred was glad to be back at work, and though his pay packet was little bigger, he had more confidence in the new safety measures at the pit. His temper sweetened and the house regained some of its serenity.

And at last Mother came home. The ambulance drew up on the earth road beside our corner house, and we all trooped down to the garden gate to give Mother a hand to the front door.

We set her down in an armchair and made her a cup of strong tea, then sat back and had a good look at her. We could see that she felt strange. She just sat there, sipping her tea, not saying anything, looking strangely shrunken.

Something was different about her. We waited uneasily for her to fit our memories of her. It was as though there were two images of Mother, swimming slightly out of focus.

Then she held out her right hand.

'Here, Alice,' she said. 'Help me off with this.'

Alice peeled off Mother's glove with some difficulty.

We all looked at the puffy white hand. Long purple scars disfigured Mother's arm, and two of her fingers wouldn't straighten properly.

'Oh, Jenny,' said Father softly. 'Oh, Jenny.'

His shoulders slumped and he turned away. I checked a shudder of revulsion and hugged Mother's head tight. She shook me off and turned to Alice.

'Come into the bedroom with me,' she said, and Alice obeyed without a word.

When they came out, Mother looked more like herself. Her step was brisk and her eyes had lost that dulled expression. I stared at her, wondering what had caused the change.

'Oh, Mother,' I said, realizing. 'It's your hair.'

She laughed, pleased that I'd noticed. The two images clicked into focus.

'That's one thing I didn't like about the hospital,' she confided. 'You couldn't take a pride in your appearance,' and she turned her fine head towards us, eyebrows raised, showing off the upswept hair style that Alice had improvised.

The arm would heal, the hand would regain its dexterity, life would go on. Father looked admiringly at his Jennie.

'Aye,' he told us. 'Nothing can happen to the family as lang as your mother can still take a pride in her appearance.'

7. Religion

THERE were only two subjects which shocked my mother, something she referred to distastefully as 'seck' and religion. It wasn't nice to talk about either.

I once asked her whether she thought there was a God. She told me that it didn't do to bother about such things. Mother was a complete pragmatist with the belief, without the compensating transport, of a Puritan. To her, life *was* a vale of tears. One accepted that and went on from there. Her outlook was essentially practical and optimistic. One 'made the best of things', one 'made the most of one's appearance', one 'managed'. Such an attitude made her capable of dealing with any emergency, but essentially she was untouched by experience. She could do the most distasteful jobs without losing her serenity. I think the source of it lay in the deep joy she received from merely being alive. She was earthy in the sense that flowers are earthy and she had a touch of their remote beauty.

Her eyes, behind their hooded lids, had an ancient look. Father used to tell us that none of us would ever be as bonny as our mother, and of course he was right, for her beauty was symbolic, as if she had frozen into the unattainable. For Mother was the least demonstrative of women.

When she lost her hearing she became even more remote from us, her world grew even narrower. She would sit in the corner, her head on one side, a tolerant smile on her lips, looking wonderfully *alive*. Her eyes would follow all our expressions and gestures, noticing everything that lay below the surface of our words, but there was a sadness in her because she couldn't live on our plane, but must always be aloof, maddeningly self-contained.

There was a charm about her appearance that communicated itself immediately, and because one couldn't give anything back to her, one felt cheated and was sometimes harsh towards her, if only to get a response.

I remember the time when a distant relative brought her small son to see 'Aunt Jennie'. Mother hated visitors because she couldn't follow strange voices, and hated being shouted at, but she smiled at the child, gave him a sweet, then ignored him. He was fascinated by this dignified woman with the sweet face. He examined her from all angles silently, for he was a shy youth, then made a tremendous effort to overcome his shyness. He took out of his pocket a long-treasured marble and presented it to Mother, who admired it absently then handed it back.

'It's for you,' he said. 'Pretty.'

Mother smiled and made no move to take it. 'Nice,' she said vaguely.

'It's yours,' he insisted, pushing it angrily towards her. 'I like you.'

This was torn from him and the confession left him furiously vulnerable.

Mother smiled fixedly, not understanding. Finally the child sobbed with frustration.

'I like you, I like you,' he yelled to the placid smiling face, beating his feet with rage.

Nothing could release his feelings but to hurl the coloured marble at Mother, who had unwittingly rejected his gift and overtures of friendship.

The marble caught her a glancing blow on the forehead, causing it to bleed slightly.

Somehow Mother had that effect on one. We must have hurt her often without leaving an actual mark on her brow, but much more deeply.

Sunday was peculiarly Mother's day. In the morning I usually went for a walk with Alice while Mother, sometimes helped by Jane, prepared the Sunday's dinner. We had meat twice a week, except in the bad times. Hotpot was Wednesday's meal and we had the 'joint' on Sundays. It was invariably a leg of mutton but each week there was anxious deliberation before the usual decision was reached. With the joint there was always fresh mint sauce, thick gravy, mashed potatoes and cabbage, with stewed fruit to follow. Sunday dinner was *the* meal of the week and everybody was there to enjoy it.

In the afternoon Alice, who was six years older than I, took me to Sunday School. Mother insisted on this, not out of deep religious convictions, but she wanted us to be exposed to religion and she also wanted her nap. After dinner we all washed up while Mother washed and changed. Appearing in her Sunday dress, with her hair (which had been kept tidily pinned up under her morning mob-cap) neatly combed and frizzed, she'd put her feet up and settle down to the Sunday paper. The ritual was always the same. Her head would sink lower and lower until it touched the table, then she'd sit up with a start and turn the page. This cat-nap was the only relaxation she enjoyed during the week, and she savoured it.

No matter how we argued, cried, or tried emotional blackmail, we *had* to go to Sunday School until we reached the age of confirmation. Appeal to Father was useless. He had his own way of spending Sunday – at the workmen's club.

So every Sunday afternoon Alice and I walked up the old abandoned railway line, bordered with pitheaps, on to the 'mission', a barracks of a hut with nothing inside but hard benches and a tuneless piano.

The walk itself was an adventure. In spring yellow coltsfoots decked the rusty lines, and in winter the pond beside the heaps used to freeze, throwing into eerie relief the withered rushes and naked black bushes. One of the pitheaps had been partly excavated for rubble and the exposed insides were red like gaping wounds in the body of the heap. Right at the top of the pit heap stood a little wooden cabin, long abandoned. I wouldn't have climbed up there for all the tea in China.

Sometimes a gang of lads, with sticks and knives stuck in their belts, would tear across the pitheaps, swoop down on us and chase us as far as the Mission.

Clutching our collection of pennies we'd go into the hut and sit on the hard little benches. The person in charge was called a captain and he wore a navy serge uniform with polished buttons. He was a very hearty individual, who had developed the terrifying technique of swooping down on one of the children, wagging a finger in their face and yelling: 'Are you for Jesus?'

We had talks about little black children, then we had to take it in turn to go up to the front and read a verse from the Bible. But the main activity of Sunday School seemed to be to yell the mission songs at the top of our voices, clapping our hands to keep time. The songs, whatever their sentiment, always had a jaunty tune. This was my favourite:

> In our work and in our play
> We keep happy all the day
> Washing dishes and ironing too
> And sometimes making Irish stew
> We do it all for Jesus
> We do it all for Jesus
> We do it ALL for Jesus
> He's done so much for me.

For years my sister and I, without conscious blasphemy, had sung the last line as

> Because he's home from work.

I suppose it made Jesus seem more real to us.

Occasionally we had a 'guest preacher', who was always a layman. One of the most memorable was Sammy Scott, a huge belly of a man with the face of a pious potato.

He used to clutch the lantern and lift it up bodily, banging it down to emphasize the points he made. He was the only one who threatened us with hell-fire if we sinned. On one occasion he pointed his finger straight at me and asked me if I was pure. Then the congregation broke spontaneously into:

> Are you washed   (yes I'm washed)
> In the blood   (in the blood)
> In the precious blood of the LAMB?
> Are your clothes quite spotless
> Are you nice and clean?
> Are you washed in the BLOOD of the LAMB?

At least that's what it sounded like, but this song and the reference to raiment 'whiter than fuller's earth' which had clothed Jesus, always made me confuse sanctity with washing-day.

When we were older, Alice and I were privileged to stay behind with the select and attend a prayer-meeting, led by Sammy Scott. He spoke movingly of the beauty of grace, but the meeting never warmed up until he'd declared war on the devil. His huge finger would point at us, his strong bellow would urge us to look around, for the devil was everywhere – even at our very elbows. Even – we held our breaths – *inside* us!

Then he'd call on us to confess our sins to God. This was the bit I liked best. I tried hard to think of some sin of such scandalous dimensions that Sammy Scott would have to pray like mad to get rid of. But I was always too self-conscious to get to my feet. I envied the ease with which the hardened sinners would lay bare their souls for us to pray over, but I couldn't think of anything to confess – except telling lies, and that seemed too ordinary to count.

The only sin I sometimes committed – one which burned like fire in my conscience, and which needed praying for – was the only one I couldn't confess because it was too shameful.

For some time now I'd been leading Alice off the straight and narrow. We each had a penny for the mission collection and my idea was that only one of us should put her penny in the bag. The other should touch the metal ring and make a metallic clink, but hold on to the penny. Each week we took it in turn to conceal the coin. On our way home we'd call in at Ganny Wilson's and buy a penn'orth of gobstoppers or hundreds-and-thousands. We never once bought the sweets on the way to the mission. I suppose some remnants of free will still clung to us.

To me then and now the taste of sin has the flavour of a mint gobstopper. My enjoyment was intensified by the sense I was doing wrong, adding a subtle sharpness to the mint flavour. Every Sunday night I'd lie awake, eaten with remorse, praying for strength to resist the temptation but succumbing the following Sunday.

So that when Sammy Scott spoke about sin I knew from experience what he was talking about. When he spoke of the devil I was out of my depth. Temptation I was familiar with – it was the desire to play truant from Sunday School. And punishment? I had personal experience of Divine vengeance.

One Sunday afternoon I quarrelled with Alice and refused to accompany her to the mission. Instead I went off on my own, over the railway bridge. Of course I took the wrong turning and wandered miserably past rows of stone houses, completely lost. It began to rain and in no time I was soaked to the skin. Crying bitterly I started to cross a road, when I ran into a cyclist and fell, bruising my knees. The pitman who had knocked me down took me to his home, where his wife gave me some tea. Eventually I sobbed out my name and address and I was taken home by bus, arriving there long after Sunday School had finished.

Mother was in a fine state, thinking I'd been abducted by one of the 'strange men' from whom I was constantly advised never to accept sweets. When she saw me coming up the path accompanied by a strange man, she nearly had a fit. To me she said nothing, except that Father would deal with me when he came home, adding darkly: 'That's what comes of not going to Sunday School.'

I was left to brood about impending vengeance, fearfully keeping an eye out for Father. He arrived home from the club later than usual. He'd had a good night and came swaying up the path, beaming beerily.

The temper of a beer drinker is very precariously balanced. He can be as benign and gentle as a kitten but one mistaken word will set him snarling savagely. When in a state of euphoria Father would throw his cap in through the doorway to see how the land lay. If it was thrown out again he knew that Mother was vexed, so he'd call one of us out and use us as a messenger to try to sweeten Mother. She displayed disapproval not by nagging but by preserving a tight-lipped silence which drove Father to distraction. Rather than suffer this ostracism, which could last for days on end, he would try to bribe her into sweetness. For Mother had a streak of personal vanity and was without means to indulge it. She would question us when we came in with Father's message ('tell her I'll give her a treat to the pictures') and was able to gauge with uncanny accuracy the precise monetary value to be reaped from his remorse. We'd be sent back with a flat refusal and Father would groan and rack his brains.

'Tell hor I'll take her into Newcastle next pay day.'

Again we'd return empty handed. The next stage was reached. Unconditional surrender.

'Ask her what she wants, hinny.'

So we'd go back to Mother, giggling conspiratorially.

'See if he's good for a blouse,' she'd say or perhaps, if he was very drunk, a hat. So Father would be let in, and the next day reminded of his promise. He'd swear then that he'd join the Rechabites and sign the pledge, but he never did. He paid up.

When I saw him coming up the path that Sunday evening, my heart sank. This time he wouldn't have to fork out. He'd merely have to assert parental authority over me and peace would reign.

When he'd grasped the situation he exaggerated his reaction, extorting full dramatic value from it.

'She never did . . . Our Mary? . . . I'll learn hor. Where's the strap?'

Solemnly it was taken down from its hook by the mantelpiece, that leather strap with which we'd all been threatened, but which I'd never known to be used. I was terrified. Father grasped me by the neck and hauled me into the scullery. Then he thumped the deal table with the strap and told me to yell, which I did with gusto. He fumbled in his waistcoat pocket and produced a tanner for me, which I knotted into my hankie, then suddenly he gave me a clout across the face which brought the tears to my eyes.

'That's for missing Sunday School,' he said earnestly. There was justice in Father's attitude, which I realized even at the time.

Mother looked with sad satisfaction at my red face and genuine tears, then led me off to bed. Everybody was satisfied.

Yes, I understood punishment for sin, but my definition was still too narrow. There must be more to it than that.

In later years I had a vague idea that sin must be connected in some way with 'seck', about which people were very reticent. Many different rumours about the facts of life were circulating among the older girls at school. When I reached confirmation, I was told, all would be clear.

Consequently, when we were fourteen, my current bosom friend and I went regularly to the confirmation classes which were held in the Infants' School hall. There were two churches in our neighbourhood – a picturesque old stone church at Craglaw, two miles away, where Father always said he'd be buried – and a new red brick affair in Rainton itself, through the railway bridge, standing just opposite the big pit at the corner ends. None of us ever went to the new church, although technically we were in its parish. On the few occasions when Alice and I were moved to attend evening service, it was to Craglaw Church that we went, mostly because we enjoyed the walk, the look of the crumbling tombstones and the sight of the choir boys. We agreed that Craglaw Church had a holier atmosphere than our parish church.

When I wanted to be confirmed I had to attend classes run by the curate of Rainton Parish Church. He was new to the diocese and accepted my presence at the classes without question. I found the course of instruction very disappointing. The curate came from down south and he had, to us, an affected manner of speech. He talked down to us and generally hummed and ha'ad until we lost interest. The facts of life were not forthcoming.

We all looked at him expectantly when he came to the bit about 'lusts of the flesh' but all he said was that if you ate too much pudding you got a stomach-ache. We lost faith in him after that, but waited with tempered expectancy for the miracle that he said would take place at confirmation. We were prepared to give it a chance, to see if it took.

'A seed is planted in you,' he intoned, 'and if it is to grow, you must water it.'

It turned out that he meant we had to go to Holy Communion. My friend and I duly went, for the experience, but she passed out during the service, faint for lack of breakfast, so I had to take her home. We decided to give up the practice. We considered that we'd given the seed a fair trial.

As far as I was concerned my seed could go down the drain. I hadn't liked the curate because to my way of thinking, nobody who had a good steady job and could afford a thick overcoat, would give much consolation to somebody on the dole. I couldn't relate religion to life – it didn't seem to come to grips with things that mattered. My philosophy at fourteen was that of the underprivileged – it's the poor that helps the poor.

When we went on the Means Test, we all reacted in a different way. Father's drinking was drastically cut down but the need for solace in beer and companionship increased. Unemployed pitmen, mufflers at neck, would congregate at the corner end outside the pub, with vacant staring eyes, sitting on their haunches. Sometimes they would talk, but when misery became incommunicable they huddled together there like lost sheep. I hated the emptiness they exuded when I walked through the group. I couldn't bear to think of Father's being one of them.

Mother had tried to tackle the situation in a practical manner. Like all country-born women, she had a strong streak of superstition in her. She either read in a newspaper, or more likely 'heard tell' of a wonderful cure for drink, strongly recommended by grateful users. Surreptitiously she sent away for this wonderful stuff. When it came she unwrapped the precious package with trembling fingers. It contained a brown powder which, the folder proclaimed, could be given harmlessly in tea. That afternoon she sprinkled a little in Father's pint pot before she filled it up with tea, then watched him anxiously while he poured the hot brew into his saucer and started to blow on it.

'Joe,' she exclaimed in sudden terror. 'Joe!'

'What's the matter, Jennie?' asked Father alarmed.

She couldn't bear to see him drink the stuff in case it was poison. She didn't try to explain or make up a story. Action came more readily to one of Mother's nature. She swept up to the table and deliberately spilt the mug of tea.

'Oh I *am* clumsy,' she muttered. 'I thought there was a fly in it.'

Later she thrust the package into the heart of the coals and raked it in vigorously. She never tried to interfere with Father's taste for beer again.

I reacted to the Means Test differently. I began to take Father's advice to 'stick in at school, lass'. It offered me a bit of hope.

As far as I could see, the only way I could ever get out of Rainton was to win a scholarship to the university. I was sick of the sight of men out of work, sick of seeing the shops boarded up, sick of the dreariness of winters without Christmas cheer.

I started walking along to the county library and studying there, for it was impossible to concentrate at home. I managed to matriculate and then there was a family conference about whether I should go out to work or try to win a scholarship and go to college.

Mother liked the idea of my working in a shop. That had been Alice's ambition but she'd had to leave school before she matriculated. I tried to convince Mother that it would be worth the extra sacrifice to keep me on at school, but I felt the unfairness of asking her and my arguments sounded thin. Then Father unexpectedly took my side.

'Let the bairn have her chance, Jennie,' he said and that settled it. I was allowed to stay on at school.

Eventually I had to apply for entrance to a college. I discovered that I had to send the Principal three references to show that I had a good character. It was stressed that one ought to be from a clergyman. I showed the form to my father.

'Clergyman?' he said musingly, looking over his spectacles. 'I know none of them fellas. Never had much to do with clergymen myself.'

I was cast into despondency at this. After working so hard, to find escape within my grasp, only to be balked by a technicality! I started to sniffle with self-pity.

'Tell ye what, lass,' said my father energetically. 'Gan alang and see the vicar and explain the situation to him. He'll give ye one.'

'What if he won't? He doesn't know me.'

'Ye can but try, hinny. Had away alang.'

So I buttoned up my school blazer and set off for the vicarage. It was a sprawling red-brick house in its own grounds, opposite the park.

I rang the bell and a parlourmaid answered the door.

'I want to see the vicar,' I mumbled, awed.

'Is he expecting you?' she inquired pleasantly.

'No,' I answered, terrified that she should shut the door. 'I've come about a reference.'

She thought that over.

'You should have an appointment,' she admonished me. 'I'll tell him you're here. What name shall I give?'

That was no help. He didn't know me from Adam.

'Tell him I'm in the parish,' I said quickly. 'The name is Craddock.'

She left me on the doorstep examining the creepers on the trellis work. Presently she came back.

'He'll spare you a few minutes,' she told me, 'if it's urgent.'

'Oh, it's urgent enough,' I groaned, then she led the way to the vicar's study. On the way I pulled at the parlourmaid's black dress.

'What's his name?' I whispered.

She gave me a sharp glance, then grinned. 'Thompson,' she whispered back. 'The Reverend William Thompson, but you'd best call him vicar. Or sir.'

That was all right. I knew where I stood now. I was ushered into a long low room with a log fire burning cheerily in the grate. There were plenty of books about and one or two framed reproductions. The vicar was sitting at a big desk which was covered with pamphlets and papers. He motioned me to take a seat opposite.

'What can I do for you?' he inquired.

He was a smallish man, running a bit to fat. I disliked his plump white hands, his carefully combed grey hair and his sharp grey eyes. I usually ignored people's appearance, preferring to make contact with the stuff of humanity lying under the surface defence put up by personality, but this one baffled me. There was nothing for my groping antennae to fix on, they slipped away unable to find a contact.

I tried bluntness.

'I've come for a reference,' I said pleasantly, as if he were a doctor who would supply me with a bottle on the panel. 'Sir,' I added.

The Reverend William Thompson looked baffled.

'But I don't *know* you,' he said, shocked.

'Oh, I'm in the parish,' I replied, trying to reassure him.

'That may be, young lady, but I've never seen you before. Don't you go to church?'

I thought it would be tactless to mention that I preferred Craglaw Church on the rare occasions when the spirit moved me. Then I saw the solution.

'I've been confirmed,' I said brightly.

The vicar looked despairingly at the ceiling.

'But you don't come to *communion*,' he wailed.

I thought about that seed that hadn't had a fair chance, and conceded the vicar's point.

'I've been too busy studying,' I replied.

The vicar put the points of his fingers together and leaned his head back until he nearly fell out of his chair. I looked at the picture of 'Madonna and Child' over the mantelpiece.

'Is that a Raphael?' I asked, curious. I was always ready to fill in gaps in my education.

The vicar took no notice. He eyed me suspiciously, then his frown cleared. He'd found a pigeon-hole to put me in.

'Tell me what you want the reference for.'

I told him that I wanted to go to college. He questioned me about my results, then he unclasped his hands and looked at me solemnly.

'God has given you a marvellous brain,' he said in parsonic tones. 'Don't you think you ought to thank Him?'

This time I was shocked and embarrassed. I shared my mother's belief that talk about religion wasn't 'nice'. What I said to God in my nightly prayers was none of the vicar's business.

'I'm prepared to write you a reference,' he went on, 'if you're prepared to come to communion.'

Nobody ever does anything for nothing. I agreed. I went home with the reference and told my father what the vicar had said. He laughed.

'Well, Mary,' he wheezed. 'You've got your reference and the vicar's found a lost sheep. Well done, Vicar. He's beaten you fair and square.'

I didn't reply.

'By the way,' he added. 'Do you know who's deed?'

I shook my head impatiently at his change of subject.

'Sidney Green, the swearing atheist. Do you mind him? Folks give him up for deed many a time but he's always hung on to life and spited them all. Till noo, that is. Died last week.'

It all came back to me – the old man in bed with a leather strap hidden under the bedclothes, and his daughter putting pressure on him to turn to the chapel for consolation. Had he finally won his battle?

'Da – how did he die?' Father understood my question.

'The same way as he lived – like he promised. Aye, he died a swearing atheist and spited the lot of them – daughter, parson and all. No preacher put anything over on Sidney Green.'

Then he added with an innocent look: 'What time shall I give you a call on Sunday?'

When Sunday came, Father woke me at seven as he'd promised, and I set off for Holy Communion.

When the vicar came round with the bread and wine I looked straight at him to make sure that he'd seen me. I'd kept my part of the bargain.

And I never went again.

8. Shabby Wedding

THERE is always something to stir a child's imagination, to fill the air
with richly glowing colours, to magic a transformation of the dull
everyday scene. Lacking toys, we children of the Means Test used our
ingenuity. We made dolls out of pegs or sticks and clothed them in
bright rags from the 'no use things' bag, and we laid them to sleep in
cardboard boxes.

Out of doors we dressed our tiny bodies in old lace curtains for the
game of 'fancy ladies' or we marked out the plan of a house in the dirt
road. Sometimes we'd carry out crackets to serve as shop counters, and
carefully set out on docken leaves our produce – pretty coloured stones
and fragments of glass to serve as jewels. We had our own form of
currency – boody, which we obtained by breaking down old saucers
or stone jam jars to the required size of the various coins.

When the weather was bad and we had to stay indoors, I had a special
private game. I would 'borrow' Ted's set of chessmen and dress them
up, then act out stories round them. I'd prettify the little white pawns
in cotton-wool, securing the fluffy skirt tightly round the waist with
silver paper. The white bishop was usually the mother, and I'd make an
elaborate dress with cellophane sweet-papers, but the *pièce de
résistance* was the mop of flowing curls I tied round her head. When
she went to the hairdresser, she had a choice, not only of style, but of

colour. She'd choose her hair from a variety of stranded cottons, then I'd thread the strand through a darning needle, wind it tightly round and fix it with a pin. The hair remained in the pin-cushion perm until the wave had taken, when it would be triumphantly knotted round her wooden head and allowed to flow in glory over her costume.

Ted did not share my enthusiasm, preferring his chessmen in the pure state. He was a serious-minded youth.

This need for grandeur, for something not utilitarian, was a natural escape from a drab environment. The beauty of certain words had power to charm me with their rich association. 'Bronze' and 'ivory' would cause me to stand entranced, experiencing a wiggle of delight, for to me they brought a sense of delicious extravagance. A sense of the forbidden reinforced the desire for beauty.

I liked certain names because of their association. Sylvia reminded me of the gleam of moonlight or the clean beauty of a silver birch. Ruby I liked because it was wine-rare, rich as blood. My favourite was Jezebel because it sounded like the tinkling of bells and the clash of cymbals.

Sometimes the urge for beauty was collective and a gang of us would gather as if at a signal, for one of our games of pageantry. Anything would serve as an excuse for dressing up. At election times we had the best excuse and we'd march round in a whirl of paper streamers over our outlandish costumes shouting out our election songs, marching in unison. And the grown-ups would encourage us, seeing in our brave display some signs of a rosier future.

Even better than the election game was our game of weddings. A profusion of weeds grew on the patch of waste land in the middle of the Black Rows. One of them grew tall and strong out of a nest of coarse leaves. When the flowers died, the plant was covered with a brittle rust fungus which we'd pull off and use as a kind of natural confetti to throw at each other. We knew the weed by no other name than 'Shabby Wedding', which has the peculiar appropriateness of most names in the North East. To a stranger travelling from one ugly mining village to the next, something of an unquenchable dignity of the people who live in them is conveyed to him by the sardonic names of 'Happy Land', 'Hope Valley', or the wonderfully stark 'No Place'.

Weddings were an enchantment to us, because they existed as things in themselves, bearing no relation to the drudgery that was to follow. A white wedding was the reward of a girl who had kept herself to herself and hadn't let anybody interfere with her. It was an incentive for virginity, for to the prudish but practical unemployed, a girl who 'got caught' had not only squandered her only treasure, but had depreciated her market value. As the old wives said: 'What man is going to buy a cow if he gets his milk for nothing?' though the more cynical of the married would advise the lovelorn: 'Never get married, hinny, and bring all your children up the same way.'

Marriage and weddings were two different things, as different as wives and sweethearts, reality and illusion. Weddings were preceded by courting, which was sheer delight. It was fitting that I should play catalyst in a courting that was to disrupt our family and bring me into touch with a social strata of whose existence I had been unaware.

I had just been weaned from the Infants' and was on my way home from the Big Girls' School, when a man stopped me just under the bridge one afternoon. Two precepts had been dinned into me from an early age – to mind the buses and never to speak to strange men – so I took no notice of him and tried to walk past.

'Hey,' said the man. 'Don't you remember me?'

I peered up at him and discovered that it was Bert Appleby, an old flame that used to flicker round Jane until she went to college. Now that Jane was doing a spell of pupil teaching locally and was living at home for a few weeks, presumably Bert wanted to get in touch with her again.

'Hallo,' I said, screwing up my face into a smile. 'I go to the Big Girls' School now.' It was always difficult to know what to say to grown-ups.

Bert, it seemed, had definite ideas about the line the conversation should take.

'Do you like sweeties?' he asked.

Did he think I was gormless? I nodded, waiting for the catch.

He held out both hands towards me. One held an envelope, the other a penny.

'Give this to Jane, then,' he said, 'and you can have the penny for sweets.'

Silently I took the note and the penny, nodded and waited for him to stand aside for me to pass. He hadn't finished with me though.

'Mind,' he warned me, 'don't let anybody else see it. Give it to Jane when she's by herself.'

'All right,' I agreed, itching to get away and spend the penny.

'Don't forget,' he called as I dashed off. 'It's a secret.'

Later, when I'd spent many agonizing minutes over my choice of sweets, and was walking slowly home, sucking meditatively, the compulsive image of Bert Appleby shadowed my thoughts.

Bert was an enigma, the youngest son of the Appleby family who lived in a big house opposite the park – in the classy end of Rainton. Bert was the apple of his mother's eye, and since she had money in her own right – her father had left her two thriving little drapers' shops – she could indulge her son to her heart's content. Bert had more liberty than the rest of the family put together, and although Mr. Appleby resented it, there was nothing he could do about it. Mrs. Appleby held the purse strings and Bert could twist her round his little finger.

His mother wasn't the only woman who found Bert irresistible, for he had a peculiar animal magnetism that worked like a charm on local girls. He had a Byronic type of good looks – startlingly pallid skin, thick black hair and moist red lips. But his charm did not lie in his colouring or in the lure of his plae blue eyes. It lay rather in the long rangy grace of his lazy stride, in the supple elegance of his body. One was always conscious of Bert's body, which he used not as an athlete, but as an animal, below the levels of consciousness.

Indeed, he had an uncanny affinity with animals. They seemed to sense in him a kindred spirit to whom they gave instinctive adoration. Bert could take a savage dog and handle it with such delicacy that it would cringe at his heels in no time, lovingly abasing itself for the kicks and cuffs he dealt it when he'd lost interest in the poor beast. Bert seemed to function on a sub-hypnotic wavelength close to nature.

He spent most of his time in the allotment which nominally earned him his keep. His mother would have given him anything to keep him at home and she made him a handsome weekly allowance in return for the vegetables and flowers he produced. When the spirit moved him he'd go off roaming the woods, dog at heel, looking for rabbits. Whether he attended his allotment or not, it didn't seem to make any difference. For Bert had green fingers.

'If you would only set your mind to it, Bert,' his father would moan, 'you could be a nursery gardener. I'd set you up in business myself, because you've got a gift for it. But you're too damned lazy, that's the top and bottom of it.'

'Leave the lad alone,' Mrs. Appleby would snap. 'There's plenty of time for him to make up his mind. Bert could make a success of anything. Let the boy enjoy himself while he's young.'

And she would be rewarded by a slow smile from her son, who had no intention of submitting to the discipline of regular hours and routine. He was allergic to hard work and was consequently impervious both to the insults of his father and the envious glances of his tradesmen brothers.

You would have expected a mother's darling with the almost pretty good looks that Bert had, to be effeminate both in looks and personality. But Bert was too indolent to bother about his appearance with the result that his tangled hair and blue chin added an exciting touch of virility to his charm. There was nothing effeminate about his interest either, for Bert had an insatiable appetite for beer and low company.

Not unnaturally, mothers warned their smitten daughters against Bert Appleby. He was regarded as a bad influence not only because of his magnetic appeal but because his language was thickly obscene and his temper ungovernable. In the pub, one minute he'd be telling filthy stories and laughing in that throaty way of his – at once degrading and irresistible – the next minute he'd be flinging the contents of his beer mug into somebody's face. Thick-skinned in some ways, nevertheless he was quick to take offence.

Inevitably this wild streak in their idol made the girls cherish the illusion that they could reform him, and they fell for him like ninepins. I suppose it was this appeal to the missionary in her that made Jane take up with him in the first place. That and the fact that she was flattered. For Bert, who normally showed no interest in the girls who threw themselves at him, had made a dead set for Jane.

There had been clandestine meetings in the park, surreptitious cuddles at Rechabite socials and one or two 'accidental' meetings in the pictures. The whole affair had been conducted on the lines of a Victorian novelette, for Jane was a romantic girl, and the novelty of it must have appealed to Bert. Then Jane had gone to college. The excitement of smuggled letters had faded, yielding to the lure of lecture notes. Jane suddenly became ambitious. She developed an acute sense of duty, reinforced by ideas of social advancement, and after examining Bert's attractions anew, she decided to make the Great Sacrifice and chuck him.

Now that she was through college and doing her spell of local pupil teaching, Jane's attractions must have gleamed anew for Bert. There was no doubt that college had added a touch of refinement to her dewy-eyed good looks, and that the flash of spirit in her had been strengthened by discipline. This combination of looks and character, spiced by unattainability, proved too strong for Bert. He was after her again – hence the note I carried.

I was aware of the danger of my mission – not for the reasons I have

set out, which I was too young to understand – but because I was uneasy about the deception I should have to practise. I was familiar with
Mother's views on marriage in general and Jane's in particular. With
Father out of work and Fred contributing so little, Jane was regarded as
an investment for the future. For this was 1930, and the General Strike,
when the miners had been betrayed, had erupted only four years back,
when I was three years old. It was natural for our parents to expect
some return from Jane, after the sacrifices they'd made to put her
through college.

It was never quite clear to whom the credit should go for Jane's
emergence into the professional classes. Father, of course, took all the
glory for himself, for his genes had provided the brains, though
Mother's lips curled in contempt of his boasting when she remembered
the pinching and scraping she'd done in order to 'manage' on a pittance
during Jane's incubation period at college. Fred, too, always asserted
that it was he and he alone, as breadwinner, who'd sacrificed his
career to 'put Jane through'. And, though this was a vague shameful
whisper, some form of financial transaction had taken place with our
formidable Aunt Brigit, who thereafter assumed the right to interfere
with our lives and give incessant advice to us on every possible occasion.

Aunt Brigit's visits were an ordeal.

There was a picture of her in the huge family album that was kept on
top of the press. Alice and I, as a special favour, were sometimes allowed
to unhook the heavy brass locks and gaze at the thick cardboard photo-
graphs of our straight-backed Victorian ancestors, who seemed to
move woodenly in an atmosphere of heavy moustaches, golden Alberts
gloriously spread across waistcoats, aspidistras and high buttoned boots.
The women appear to have been excessively fond of jet, little frilly
lace capes, lockets and brooches shaped like hearts.

Father was full of scandalous stories about them, and though
Mother usually laughed with shocked delight, she was always deferen-
tial about Aunt Brigit and Uncle Fred, in honour of whom her first
son had been named.

'A fine figure of a man,' she'd sigh, admiring the portly figure of her
brother in napoleonic attitude against a painted balustrade. 'Worked
himself up to be one of the chief men in Conley Iron Company.
And sharp as a needle. Nobody put anything across your Uncle
Fred.'

'Except Aunt Brigit,' Father would mutter testily. 'She saw *him*
coming.'

And while Mother bridled at this disloyalty, Father would lay his finger on the photograph, turning to us impressively.

'Look at that great neb on her. Alice – Mary – mark what I say. Never trust anybody with a nose like that. It's a sartin sign of a nasty disposition. Amn't I right, Jennie?'

Secretly Mother shared his view, for in her eyes nobody would have been good enough for her adored brother Fred, but family loyalty was strong in her.

'Nothing at all of the sort, Joe. I'm surprised at you talking like that to the bairns. Your Aunt Brigit,' she'd insist to us, 'is a highly thought-of woman. A noble-looking woman.'

'Eeh now, Jennie,' Father would cry, certain of his ground, 'she's got a face on her like the back end of a bus. She's not a patch on thee for looks.'

And Mother, pleased, would tweak her fringe, though she made a pretence of demurring.

Father, overriding her 'get away with you Joes', would come back strongly with an attack on Brigit's two offspring, who simpered anaemically at the camera. Here Mother was with him.

'Look at them two soft Jessies.' Alice and I would gaze contemptuously at our rivals – our own two well-off cousins. 'Al-bert' – in Father's mouth the name was an embodiment of sissiness – 'a proper little mammy's boy, ower soft to clag. And as for that one – '

Words failed him as he contemplated Hettie's vacant prettiness. He took refuge in vague forebodings: 'What'll come of that one I *don't* know. I sometimes wonder if she's all reet in the heed.'

Mother thought this was going a bit too far. Hettie may be a flapper, indulged at home because she wasn't clever enough to earn her living at a 'respectable' job, but she had her points.

'She thinks the world of Jane,' she pointed out. Indeed Hettie had an outsize crush on my clever sister, and made her the recipient of her infantile confidences.

'And so she should,' Father agreed roundly. 'Jane's a young *woman* and Hettie's still a bairn. Arrested development – that's what it is. There's only three years difference between them, but the way that Hettie gans on, you'd think she was still in the baby class.'

'Let the lass enjoy herself while she's young,' said Mother complacently. 'She'll most likely find some young fellow and settle down soon enough.'

A worried expression flitted momentarily across her face then vanished as as she added briskly: 'Jane's got too much sense to pay any attention to Hettie's prattle – boys this, boys that and boys the other. Jane's got her heart set on a *career*.'

It was this attitude of my parents towards the male sex that made me wary and sin-conscious as I hopped home with Bert's note. In a house as open as ours, secrecy was well nigh impossible, but I did the best I could and pushed the envelope down behind Jane's modesty vest when she was sorting out her lesson notes.

I found out later that it wasn't a love letter at all – Bert had too much sense to subject his illiterate scrawl to Jane's educated eyes. He'd hit upon something much more subtle.

He'd sent Jane a ticket to a dance at the Store Hall, hoping that her natural liveliness, coupled with a dislike of seeing good money wasted, would persuade her to spend an evening in his company. Bert had calculated Jane's reaction shrewdly, but the chief appeal of his manoeuvre was its air of secrecy. It was this, reinforced by Jane's innate caution, that caused her to make an accomplice of Hettie. Nobody could object to the two cousins having a night's relaxation at a local hop – except Father, but Mother talked him round. So Jane had it all ways – parental permission, heroine worship from Hettie, and the joy of an illicit meeting with the attractive but forbidden Bert.

I remember the day of the dance most clearly. Hettie came down by bus in the afternoon, then she and Jane set to with such a prinking and tong-curling and giggling that Father went off early to the club in disgust, muttering: 'There's nowt to choose between them. That Hettie has got our Jane as daft as herself.'

He made sure to insist that they were back from the dance by ten o'clock sharp, however. He didn't share the modern view that if there's bad in a girl it will come out at two o'clock in the afternoon as easily as at two o'clock at night. Father was a firm believer in the cloistered virtue.

When he'd gone, it was a signal for gaiety and high spirits. Mother furtively produced a box of powder that she kept well-hidden from Father, who'd have thrown the 'ket' at the back of the fire. She was as gay as the two girls, giving advice on the choice of sash or necklace with excited authority. Alice seated herself firmly in front of the mirror and plastered her face with lipstick and I remember being infected by the high spirits and screaming at the top of my lungs for a dab of powder on my nose.

The greatest transformation was in my brother Fred, who suddenly revealed a boisterously playful side. Hettie's empty laugh rang out frequently at his sallies which were accompanied by heavy nudges and playful slaps. Frivolity was given its head that day, and Jane and Hettie, flushed with excitement, twinkled with glamour.

Of course Alice and I – the bairns – were in bed long before the grown-ups came home from the dance, but bit by bit we pieced together what had happened. Fred had gone along too as chaperon and had had a whale of a time with young Sadie Pratt, a pert-tongued young miss who knew her own mind and everybody else's.

There'd been an animated discussion in the kitchen before Father came back from the club, all about who was getting off with whom, and putting people in their places and where everybody was during the interval. Hettie was in her bright-eyed element, panting like a bird at Fred and fluttering round Jane in an ecstasy of admiration. Then a bed was made up in the kitchen for Jane and Hettie, so that when Father stamped in, a false air of innocent conformity concealed the beating hearts.

Next morning Hettie went back to Conley Bridge, Fred woke up in his usually surly mood and Jane threw herself into her school work with feverish vigour, like a penitent pleading for another chance. Even Mother wore a faintly guilty flush and bustled about chasing the dirt out with even more than her usual vehemence.

Father alone said nothing – pointedly. He ignored us all except young Ted, who alone had been unaffected by the *decensus averno* and whom he treated gravely as an equal, the only adult in the family.

Sensitive to the prevailing atmosphere, I hurried furtively down back streets on my way to and from school, trembling lest I should encounter temptation in the form of grinning Bert Appleby. Jane increased her efforts for the Rechabites and after tea used to explain to me the meaning of her brightly coloured religious tracts.

All would have been well if Hettie, well-intentioned foolish Hettie, had not intervened. Her novelettish mind saw Jane being diverted from the path of True Love, and she took it upon herself to act as cupid.

'You seem to have a lot of spare time on your hands, lass,' Father said pointedly to Hettie on one of her frequent visits. 'More than Jane has, anyway.'

Hettie writhed in embarrassment, her blue eyes popping with cunning.

'I thought mebbe Jane would like a bit fresh air, Uncle Joe. I thought a walk up to the park might clear her head.'

'Some folks heads doesn't need clearing,' said Father. 'Fresh air's the worst thing in the world for brains. Turns them rusty. Same as watter rusts a stomach.'

Hettie giggled in a deflated way, but then Mother intervened.

'Jane *is* looking a bit peaky at that. A walk out wouldn't do her any harm. Give them books a rest for a bit.'

Jane's nerves and consequently temper, hadn't been too steady of late. I prudently kept out of the way of her sharp tongue.

'I'd be all right if you just left me alone,' she snapped, then turned grimly to Hettie. 'Come on then, let's get out of this.'

Hettie meekly followed Jane out of the house, hovering like a placating shadow behind her idol's angry back. She was obviously going to feel the lash of Jane's unbridled tongue.

But Hettie wasn't as green as she was cabbage-looking. She led Jane to a rendezvous with Bert and left the two of them illicitly together in the bowling green shelter.

That summer was shot with golden days. Jane finished her teaching practice and went dreamily back to college for her last term. When she came home for her last vacation before she started her probationary period of pupil teaching at Allanvale, she looked as if life had no more to offer her. She, Jane Craddock, was going to reward Mother for all her sacrifices during the years of poverty, she and she alone would support the family and vicariously restore's Father's self-respect. For Fred was only a young pitman, whose money barely supported himself and Dad's dole was microscopic.

'What a difference this will make to you,' she promised Mother. 'Now the others shall have their chance. I'll see Ted through – I give you my word. I'll do the same for him as you did for me.'

Honeyed words dropped from her lips like largesse, and Fred clenched his big fists broodily.

'Ye'll have to stop chasing about the roads with Bert Appleby then,' he said viciously. 'Or else nobody will have a chance.'

Suddenly his resentment flared into temper. Angrily he thumped the back of the horsehair couch in short ugly jabs, fiercely trying to free himself from incoherence.

'Ted will get his chance, will he? And what chance did *I* ever get? Tell me that. None – not one bloody chance at all. No – I'm Joe Soap in this family. Treated like muck in me own home, cos I'm a common pitman. What about the sacrifices I*'ve* made? What about the chances *I* could have had? Tell me that.'

'Shut your daft gob,' said Father angrily. 'Thoo'd never have made anything of theself. Thoo's nee bloody good as a *pitman*. All thoo's good for is sitting on thy backside and yelling at your mother to come out and wait on thee. Sacrifices?' He spat.

When he was beside himself, Father's accent broadened. It was unusual to see him lose his temper and Fred's jaw dropped in surprise, at Father's usurping *his* privilege. But it wasn't Fred's outburst that had unsettled Father – it was his reference to Jane.

'What's all this aboot thoo and Bert Appleby?' he said quietly, fixing Jane with a steady blue eye.

The look that Jane gave Fred contained contempt, betrayal and a declaration of the war that was to last between them for years. All the shared complicity of youth dropped from her as her attitude to Fred crystallized into dislike. Then she turned to Father.

'There's nothing between me and Bert Appleby,' she said with dignity. 'I'm not interested in him. I'm not to blame if he made a fool of himself about me. Surely you can trust me not to throw away everything I've worked for on a worthless piece of rubbish?'

Her voice, which had held quiet authority, became shrill, her protests too loud to carry conviction. Mother stepped quietly towards her.

'We trust you, Jane,' she said soothingly. 'Your Father just wants to know how things stand, that's all.'

She turned to Fred, who was standing like a stuffed duck, gaping as Defarge might, when an aristocrat had escaped the guillotine.

'I think you should apologize to your sister,' said Mother sharply, 'for all the mischief you've caused.'

This was too much for Fred.

'Me apologize to that stuck-up piece? Like hell I will. She's the one that should apologize – for telling downright lies. It's all over Rainton about her and Bert Appleby. It's a bloody scandal.'

Jane sniffed contemptuously.

'I've never been out alone with him,' she said with finality, in answer to Father's worried look. 'He's making it all up. Hettie always came too.'

'That's good enough for me then,' said Father. 'Look here, Fred. I've heard enough from you. Noo if ye take my advice – '

'You know what you can do with your advice. Fancy letting that toy make a fool of you. Advice? She's the one that needs advice. She needs a good kick on the backside into the bargain. But will she get it? Not on your life. I tell you, I'm sick and tired of the way you all suck up to our Jane. Just because she's been to college.'

He spat the word, then added darkly: 'I hope you get some good of her college eddication. Ye might find that you picked the wrong one to have her chance.'

Father sighed wearily at the familiar tirade, maddening Fred further.

'So I'm not even good enough for the bloody pits, am I not?' Hurt pride made him venomous. 'I'll surprise you yet, never you mind. You'll be laughing at the other side of your face one of these days. You'll find you've lost your Joe Soap. I've a good mind to clear out and leave you flat.'

'Where would you go?' put in Jane spitefully.

'Anywhere that's a lang way from here, that's a fact. Canada or Australia. There's no future in this bloody country.'

Self-pity and frustration made his anger impotent. His big arms hung loosely at his sides. In the sudden silence that followed his wounded bellow, he stamped over to the door.

'Where are you off to?' Mother's voice was sharp with anxiety, but Fred didn't even answer.

'Let him be,' said Father. 'He'll cool off somewhere, then come back soon enough. I've never known Fred miss a meal.'

'He'll be off after that Sadie Pratt,' said Mother unexpectedly. 'She'll make him worse. There's a pair of them – one's as bad as the other for spiting folks.'

'She's welcome to him,' Father spat into the fire, then got up. 'I'm away alang to the club.'

'That's men folks for you,' sighed Mother as the door closed behind Father. 'Get everybody worked up, then go off and enjoy themselves. I don't know.'

The silence was very restful. Jane went over and put her arm round Mother's slumped shoulders.

'You've finished with that chap then?' asked Mother quietly.

Jane nodded.

'He was no good to you.'

Jane's silence accepted the fact.

'Not that that makes any difference,' said Mother with a slight smile.

Jane gave Mother a sharp look, then her lips took on an identical curve, as if they shared a secret knowledge.

'I'm well out of it,' she said firmly.

Hettie was terribly disappointed when she heard about Jane's decision. But suddenly Hettie and Bert and Sadie Pratt sank into insignificance, their puffed-up importance blown away like meaningless froth as we came up against the basic realities.

The Means Test man called.

Cold, hard, official facts exposed Jane's pipe-dream for what it was. Her starting salary would barely support herself, let alone the family. To crown it all, she wasn't even allowed to come home at week-ends and help us out then. Jane's cherished contribution was to be swallowed up by digs. A stranger was to benefit from Mother's self-denial.

'There's nobody we can turn to,' said Mother wearily. 'We're back where we started. It's all been for nothing.'

Climbing off the poverty level during the depression was a labour of Sisyphus. But once you gave in you lost that priceless intangible, self-respect.

So Jane weaved her little plots of sneaking home at odd week-ends and slipping Mother the forbidden pound 'to help out'. And Father made a grotesque figure of fun out of the 'queer fella' whose distasteful duty it was to pry into our affairs. He even made a joke of his own fruitless attempts to get work, but it couldn't have been easy to face Fred's sardonic tongue when Father came in weary from the endless humiliations of countless refusals after tramping the streets offering to do anything for a bob or two. There were too many able-bodied youngsters on to that game, with as little success as Father.

We were so preoccupied with our own problems that we forgot about other people, so Aunt Brigit's unexpected visit came on us like a bombshell. There was nothing in the house to offer her except a cup of tea, which she refused. She sat upright on the sofa, her black dress rustling with sympathetic indignation, peering at my parents over her rimless spectacles.

'I expect you know what I've come about,' she began without preamble.

Mother looked at Father listlessly for enlightenment. He shrugged, puzzled. Aunt Brigit sniffed at his appearance – for he was in shirt-sleeves and muffler and hadn't yet shaved – and went on grimly: 'I suppose you've been too *busy* to see what's been going on under your very noses.'

Father looked at her with as much dignity as he could muster, but he was no match for her aggressive neatness.

'Come to the point,' he told her quietly.

'It's Hettie.'

'What aboot Hettie?' asked Father in some surprise. He had enough on his plate, he implied, without thinking about that flighty creature.

'She's going to get married.' Aunt Brigit snapped the words out, but there was triumph in her tone.

'Eeh, now,' said Father gently, giving Brigit his full attention. 'Nivor the world.'

Mother leant forward in her chair, certain she'd misheard, raising her eyebrows at Father for elucidation.

'Now you come to mention it,' he went on. 'I haven't seen Hettie aroond here for a bit. I gave her the sharp end of me tongue and she's taken the huff with me.'

He folded his arms and leant back in his chair, smiling.

'So she's hooked a fella for herself. Who's she got ahold of?'

'Bert Appleby.'

'What?' Father jerked forward to the edge of the chair. 'D'ye hear that, Jennie? Hettie's gannin to wed Bert Appleby.'

'I thought you knew all about it,' said Brigit in some bewilderment, then bridled. 'Is this one of your tricks, Joe Craddock, pretending to know nothing about it, when you're the one that's responsible?'

'Noo – hold on a minute there, Brigit,' said Father firmly. 'What's it got to do with me? What's at the back of your mind?'

Then he stopped and said slowly: 'When's the wedding?'

Brigit clicked her handbag shut with bitter satisfaction.

'As soon as possible.'

'Ooh – it's like that, is it? And I hadn't the faintest idea.' Then he seemed to become aware of Brigit's pent-up fury. 'What d'ye mean *I'm* responsible? It's nowt in the world to do with me.'

'You should have looked after the girl. She was in your charge when she came down here,' spat my formidable aunt. 'That's a fine return I must say for all I've done for you.'

That put the fat in the fire. Father's eye gleamed with the light of battle, but before he could open his mouth, Mother intervened.

'Well, we can't make any better of it now,' she pointed out. 'The damage is done, and Brigit seems to have made the best of it. I suppose you had a bit of job persuading him?'

Brigit turned with relief to Mother.

'I went down to see his parents. They wouldn't believe me at first, but I soon showed them their duty. They knew they wouldn't have any peace until Bert did the right thing.'

Her nose sharpened in memory of the scene.

'We came to an arrangement. We've both put so much by as a wedding present on condition they go away from the district.'

'Some folks has all the luck,' muttered Father. 'So you've given them a start?'

'I've done my duty,' replied Brigit stiffly. 'But she's no daughter of mine now.'

Mother nodded in agreement. The Code must be obeyed. The disgrace must be hushed up. The two women's minds moved along the same groove.

'And the wedding?' said Mother. 'You'll want a splash, I suppose?'

'She'll have a proper send off,' agreed Brigit. 'And I want all the family there. Everything's got to look right.'

Father snorted at this female hypocrisy and left the two women to their planning. He had his own opinion of Brigit, and as soon as the woman had gone, he tackled Mother.

'I won't have you running after Brigit like this,' he said testily. 'She's nowt to do with us. Let her stew in her own juice.'

Mother returned mildly: 'She's done a lot for our Jane. It's up to me to give a hand now.'

Father had been brooding about an ancient wrong.

'She did no more than her duty to us,' he insisted. 'And it was only guilty conscience that made her do that.'

Many a time he'd told us the tale, of how when grandfather lay dying from a stroke which bereft him of speech, Aunt Brigit wouldn't let anyone else in the room where she nursed him.

'What became of your grandfather's gold sovereigns?' he'd ask rhetorically.

'Hidden in the mattress I'll be bound,' and we'd wait for the explanatory aside to us – ''cos they didn't believe in banks in them days, you see.'

Like a refrain came Mother's insistent, 'Now, Joe, you know there was no proof.'

And he'd wag a forefinger at her and go on: 'His eyes would watch her all ower the bedroom.' His own eyes would widen in a pantomime of helplessness, then narrow to express diabolical cunning as he went on: 'And there she was – searching that room while the old man lay sick in bed. The old bitch.'

In the dramatic pause that followed, Mother would again mutter about proof, then Father would triumphantly shout her down. 'Proof? What about the slit in the mattress? What more proof do you want? And Brigit didn't waste any time. The old man wasn't cold in his grave before she'd bought that big house at Conley Bridge. That's proof enough for me.'

And to all the arguments and accusations of being jealous of Uncle
Tom's success at the Iron Company, Father would shake his head,
thinking of that slit in the mattress.

Mother didn't dwell on the fact that we should do what we could to
help Aunt Brigit out. It was no use appealing to Father's gratitude for
Brigit's timely help to Jane.

'Conscience money or not,' she said. 'We were mighty glad of it at
the time. And I'm going to do my bit.'

So the whole family turned up at Conley Bridge, for a wedding that
took our breaths with its magnificence. I'd never seen as much food in
my life before, and though Father muttered that it was a sin to 'hoy
money aback of the fire' when times were so bad, yet the memory of
it lives yet.

Amid all the richness of food and colour, Jane stood out like a sore
thumb. She stood pale and quiet in her sober dress, while Hettie pranced
around in a float of chiffon, giggling at everything.

Jane only spoke to Bert once. That was when he forced a drink on
her for old time's sake.

'Forget the pledge for once,' said Bert, whose eyes were bright with
booze. 'And give us a toast.' He put an arm familiarly over her shoulder, and Jane shivered, shaking it off.

'All right, then,' she agreed, looking straight into those animal eyes.
'I'll toast the happy couple. May you get what you deserve.'

We left soon after that. Father had been itching to get home, feeling
out of place in the fat *bourgeois* atmosphere, sickened by Brigit's
false hospitality. Jane came with us. She'd had enough. But Fred stayed
on to enjoy the company of Sadie Pratt, whose bright malicious eyes
had mocked at Jane's chagrin, all the afternoon. Alice and I had been
rapt in ecstatic awe, amazed at the comfort in which some people
lived, gloating over the wasteful glitter of the reception.

'It was lovely,' breathed Alice at last, breaking the silence that divided
the adults into brooding separateness. 'Isn't Hettie lucky?'

All three adults looked at Alice's flushed face as if her remark had
taken them aback with its simplicity. They avoided each other's eyes.
The bright look faded from Alice's face and she looked towards them
nervously for enlightenment.

Father spoke, and that was all anybody said to us on the subject.
'Hettie? I doubt she's swopped her fiddle for a gew-gaw.'

The wedding was over. The flapper was caught.

9. The Slum Clearance

JUST after I started at the Grammar School, I became aware that I lived in a slum. Authority had dealt a succession of blows at our independence, circumscribing our lives.

First there had been the visit of the 'queer fella' from the Means Test. The effect of this was to outlaw Jane from the family, apart from the forbidden visits which she made on rare week-ends. The indirect effect was to throw Fred straight into the arms of Sadie Pratt, who led him by the ear into holy deadlock.

The family seemed shrunken, but Ted was growing apace and Alice and I made enough trouble for six. We were still a family and the Black Rows was still our home. Then the local council – Authority again – decided to pull down the old wooden houses and erect streets of terraced council houses.

To me the slum clearance is always linked with the affair of Dippy Dotty, the backward daughter of Ted Johnson, the old miner who loved his drop of beer. Poor chap, he needed it with the life Dotty led him.

Father, who knew all the gossip in Rainton – and what he didn't know he invented – told Mother all about it in bed one night. We could hear his careful tones through the far room wall as he confided this secret into her good ear.

'They fetched a fella to see Dotty yesterday,' he said conspiratorially.

'Oh?' Mother's voice pricked with interest.

'They gave her some sort of test to see if she'd have to be put away.'

The message was received and understood.

'Will they take her to Meadowfield then?' asked Mother. Meadowfield was the euphemistic name of the nearest lunatic asylum.

'No,' whispered Father loudly. 'She got the better of them. They asked her what was the difference between a stone and an egg.'

'Between a stone and a what? A bed?'

'An egg – EGG.' Father was shouting now, and Mother's reply was offended.

'Oh – an egg. What did she say?'

All of us in the far room were listening now.

'She's not that gormless. She gave them one of her looks and telt them that you could eat an egg.'

We joined in with Mother's appreciative giggle.

'Go to sleep there, you bairns,' shouted Father, and that was the end of the conversation.

Dorothy Johnson's birth had been a mistake. Folks said that Mrs. Johnson had tried to get rid of the child. All agreed that something had gone wrong with the birth. After a painful labour, Mrs. Johnson gave birth to Dotty.

The child had never been normal. She left school at the age of twelve when she was still in the Infants. Dotty was a big, fat, glowering lump of a girl with a lazy disposition and a vile temper. She drove her mother to distraction and her father to drink.

Clad in a filthy old sack apron, with misshapen boots on her bare feet and a huge smear of soot over her face, she'd spend most of the morning telling the neighbours about how badly treated she was at home. To look at her you'd think that she did all the work in creation, and when Mrs. Johnson, who never gossiped, always appeared so neat and clean, it gave credence to Dotty's story. Towards everybody but her own family, Dotty displayed a peculiar kind of slow charm. The more shiftless of the neighbours would welcome her into their homes and give her something sweet to eat, for Dotty had an insatiable appetite. In exchange for food she'd spin malicious stories about her mother and father.

To the gangs of children who roamed the Black Rows, Dotty was fair game. A popular sport was to line up outside Johnson's back door and chant, 'Dippy Dotty, Dotty's dippy,' until she came charging out at us like a bull. On rare occasions she came at us armed with a poker, but she was easy to dodge because of her lumbering fatness. She'd charge at us, cursing at the top of her voice, threatening what she'd do to us if she ever caught us, with tears of rage streaming down her dirty face.

But nobody really minded Dotty except her parents. She wasn't our responsibility. The news that she might be 'taken away', however, caused us for the first time to look upon her as a human being. In a way, the Black Rows wouldn't be the same without her.

Her romances caused us a good deal of amusement. Dotty had once had a crush on the mission captain, and every Sunday she'd sit hugely amongst the children, gazing adoringly at the poor man, with a soppy smile spread over her daft face like a smear of jam. When she took to hanging around the mission gate on the off chance of meeting him, the poor fellow developed a hunted look. He asked for a transfer shortly after she'd made him a laughing stock by trying to hold his hand at a Sunday School outing. As he pointed out to the vicar at the time, he didn't mind giving the children a treat, but there were limits.

The Johnsons worried about Dotty's pashes on the most unlikely people. When she went off to the pictures, they'd wait outside to see that she wasn't picked up by some unscrupulous man. They tried to conceal themselves in doorways because if Dotty saw them following her she'd stand stock-still in the middle of the crowd, cursing and yelling at her parents for spying on her.

'I'm not a child,' she would cry. 'I'm a grown woman.'

People would gather round her sympathetically and her parents would feel like Simon Legree.

Mrs. Johnson must have been at the end of her tether when she sent for the medical officer. She was only a little body, whereas Dotty was growing powerfully strong, as if she fretted away at her mother's nerves and used them for nourishment. Every evening she'd sit clocking in the armchair, keeping up a continuous monologue about real and imaginary grievances, casting glances of hatred at her mother who sat motionless except for the fitful twitch of the vein in her brow.

Mr. Johnson could keep his daughter in check but it took so much out of him that he had to escape to the pub to recover. It was when the door clicked behind him that Mrs. Johnson's twitch grew worse and her eyes flicked round the room in panic. For Dotty was becoming physically violent, and mustn't be crossed.

Then Dippy Dotty found a friend. In a way Sally Maddison was just as much of an outcast as Dotty. She was a quiet mousy creature who'd been in service at the 'Hall' and had come home to look after her father until she got another 'situation'. To the best of my knowledge Sally hadn't spoken a word to a soul all her life. She was a frightened little body always tacitly apologizing for her own existence, making even the most tender-hearted feel sadistic.

Dotty thought she was marvellous. The two of them used to go off to the park together and sit there for hours content with each other's company. Dotty learned things from Sally that she'd refused with curses to learn from her mother. She allowed Sally to cut her tangled mop of hair, and started taking a well-intentioned but misguided interest in her appearance. Sally used to call for her on Sundays and cart her off to church, after which Mrs. Johnson heaved a sigh of relief.

The two of them were inseparable until one day the Labour Exchange found a suitable opening and Sally had to go back into service. Her departure didn't raise a ripple in the life of Rainton – she'd slipped out of it as she'd come in, like a self-effacing ghost. Sally had the knack of appearing on the scene as if she wasn't really there, so it took us all some time to notice the fact that she'd gone.

But the difference in Dotty's life was tremendous. The sun had stopped shining for her when Sally went away. All day long she moped in the scullery, stuffing herself with anything she could lay hands on, as if to seek consolation in food.

About a month after Sally left, I had to call at Johnson's for the union money. I rattled the scullery sneck, but nobody came to the door.

'Had away,' shouted a gruff voice.

I peered in at the window, to see Dotty sitting on the cracket, with her apron full of nut shells, munching away for dear life.

'Is your mother in, Dorothy?' I shouted.

I don't know what induced me to call her by her Sunday name. Maybe because she looked so forlorn among the discarded monkey-nut shells.

Dotty straightened herself, giving her pinny a shake, then came to the door crushing the shells underfoot with a glorious indifference. She put her head round the door and examined me suspiciously, sucking her teeth to free them of nuts.

Instead of giving my usual cheeky grin, I looked embarrassed. Dotty was equally shy. Shorn of her usual defence of swearing and blasting me, communication was at a dead end. She stood twisting a corner of her sack apron while she groped for words.

'Come in,' she grunted at last. 'Sit yourself doon.'

I went formally into the living-room and seated myself at one side of the fireplace, facing her.

'Is your mother out?' I asked primly.

'She's at the shops.'

Speaking to Dotty as an adult was like trying to express myself in a foreign language. There was a strange air of formality about the occasion. Dotty sat opposite watching me expectantly. I must think of something to say, if only to break Dotty's fearsome concentration. I looked round furtively for something to release me.

'That's a nice vase,' I said, pointing at random to a hideous ornament on the sideboard.

A beautific smile transfigured Dotty's sullen features.

'Sally gave me that,' she said with dreadful eagerness. 'For a keepsake when she went away. Here!'

She grabbed me by the hand and hauled me upstairs. Unwittingly I had found the key to Dotty's secret places of the heart. Such monumental trust, such elephantine eagerness pole-axed me. I was terrified. Her hand on my arm was like a clamp.

Inside her room she turned to the chest of drawers in the corner and rummaged about, muttering childish incantations. I edged towards the door with extreme caution.

'I've got to be going,' I said quickly, finding myself incapable of adding 'Dorothy', lest it should lead to further dreadful developments.

Dotty took no notice. She was making a little pile of things on the bed. Curiosity made me draw nearer.

It was a strange little collection. A Christmas card hoarded for at least ten years, a bottle of cheap scent with a tassel round its neck, a hymn book, a strap of bright beads and a postcard. The latter looked new, so I bent forward to pick it up.

Dotty snatched the card away and allowed me to admire the side featuring a coloured picture of a kitten while she laboriously read out the message printed in capitals on the other side.

'All the best. Love, Sally,' she intoned, breathing heavily, then, after wiping the glossy side of her sack apron, she put the card carefully back in the drawer. She fumbled around a bit and finally produced a pair of knitting needles with a few painful lines of purple knitting straggling from them.

'This is a kettle-holder,' she explained, peering at me earnestly. 'For Sally. *She* taught me how to knit.'

Again she gave me that questioning, groping look.

'She'll like that,' I gabbled with patently false enthusiasm. 'It's nice and bright.'

Hysterical laughter was bubbling in my throat like phlegm. Purple! But Dotty was partial to bright colours. I turned away from that fixating gaze, conscious that something more was expected of me. I was completely out of my depth.

In the silence the sneck of the back door clapped like thunder and I turned my back on the waiting Dotty as if I'd just been released from a sleeping spell. Even as I clattered down the uncarpeted stairs I knew that my flight was a betrayal.

Mrs. Johnson was surprised to see me enter but I babbled an explanation and waited tensely for her to find the necessary coppers and the union card. Dotty remained in her room and as I held out my hand in relief for the green card, I heard the decisive click of the bolt being shot in her bedroom. Dotty had not only locked herself in with her keepsakes, she'd locked everybody else out.

That was the last time I saw Dotty. She was knocked down by a bus a week later and died without regaining consciousness. I suppose she'd wanted to die. As the old wives pointed out, there was no future for her, she was better off the way she was. Life was a trial at the best of times and it was a mercy she was spared worse. And so on. There's always a platitude to fit the occasion.

Mrs. Johnson pottered around with a dazed look for some time afterwards, timidly avoiding her neighbours. Her gaze slid away from you when you spoke to her, and not a few of the neighbours started muttering about 'guilty consciences'. Dotty's faults faded with the flowers on her grave, and most people felt that a part of the Black Rows had gone with her.

I brooded about her death, because I felt personally involved. Sudden and violent death was not an unheard-of thing in our neighbourhood. There was plenty to try the spirit of a man during the depression, and some found that a rope in the lavatory was the easiest way out. Failing that, there was always the pond up by the pit heaps. It was usually a woman's body that was dragged out of the pit pond. The uninviting stretch of stagnant water, symbolized for her an escape from an intolerable situation, so she would duck under the wire-netting fence and slither into the filthy pond, seeking nirvana among the dead dogs and tin cans that lay there already. And for girls in trouble there was the lure of the lysol bottle.

No, it wasn't the manner of Dotty's death that worried me. Anybody could be knocked down by a bus. Far from being a shock, it made her death an irrelevance. What upset me was the feeling that Dotty's life was unfinished. She'd laid an obscure claim on me which I had sidestepped, and there was nothing that I could ever do to alter it.

I went to collect the union money shortly after Dotty's funeral. Mrs. Johnson was sitting quietly in the rocking-chair and when I went in she raised lack-lustre eyes in my direction. I explained my errand and stood waiting. As if against my will, my eyes were drawn to the hideous vase on the sideboard. Mrs. Johnson saw me looking at it and tottered over to pick it up. She walked like an old woman now.

'This was Dorothy's,' she said in a faint smile. 'She thought the world of it.'

I nodded, because I wanted to clear my throat and couldn't.

Dotty's mother stood with the vase in her hands, rubbing the sides with her thumbs in a meaningless gesture. The fire hissed and sputtered.

'Your own flesh and blood,' she whispered. 'Your own flesh and blood.'

Her eyes slid away from the vase towards my face.

'Here,' she said, holding the vase out towards me. 'I'd like you to have it. You wasn't like some of the others. Take it away with you.'

I backed away instinctively, but there was something compelling in the little black-shawled figure of Mrs. Johnson. I found myself with the vase in my hands, and as I took it, I seemed to hear the click of a bolt from an upstairs bedroom. A keepsake from Dotty. I wonder what happened to the pile of treasures on the bed.

Dotty's funeral marked the end of the old way of life in the Black Rows. A week later the 'Cooncil' started to pull down the empty row of wooden houses that looked on to the main road. Then on the site they built a block of six double-storeyed councils in red brick, and the first of the Black Rowites moved in. We all turned out to watch the removal and the six chosen families, very conscious of the mixture of envy and sardonic amusement their exodus caused, took up their new abode in style.

Demolition and building went on simultaneously, and everybody's life had a picnic quality. Gangs of workmen threw up huge piles of stone and rubble, so in the evenings gangs of children had a fine time playing explorers on Everest. There was the added danger of the pits of white lime the builders used. Horrible stories of what happened if you fell in dominated our imaginations, rivalling quicksands for horror.

Compulsively we gathered round the lime-pits and peered in, fascinated, then went off to wander about in the shells of the old wooden houses. The plaster-smelling new red bricks didn't interest us. It was too much like our own game of marking out house outlines in the dirt, and it posed the same teasing question. What happens when the house is marked on the earth path, what happens when the red-brick houses are finished? Uneasily we watched the little toy rooms grow up like boxes. I sought out Father for information.

'What's it all for?'

'It's the slum clearance,' he explained. 'The Black Rows has been condemned.'

I took the word away to brood about it. Condemned – it had an ugly ring. As Alice and I, wandering the earth paths at night, nostalgic for our lost freedom, roamed among the desolate shells of the old homes and let our voices echo distortedly from the crazily hanging rafters, I whispered the word 'condemned' to myself. I thought I knew what it meant. It had the same smell of fear and authority as 'Means Test' had and its meaning embraced the smell of old people, loneliness and the workhouse. The condemned houses stood unsteadily with bowed shoulders, like men in the dole queue.

I slid a look at Alice, then picked up a loose lath and smashed a window pane, setting glass fragments flying in all directions.

'Condemned,' I muttered viciously. 'Depression. Bloody,'' swearing all the bad words out of my system with each blow, until Alice took the lath off me and led me away along the new concrete path.

Much as we had loved the ill-lit mystery of the Rows, and however painful our sense of loss, there was excitement with the newness of the estate. Things were changing and must therefore be improving. Although, being children and therefore naturally conservative, we didn't share Father's buoyant optimism, we liked its manifestation. As usual it took a practical turn.

The plan of the estate was taking shape. Neat blocks of houses were arranged in geometrical patterns at either side of the new roads. At every right-angled bend a street lamp was strategically placed. All was sweetness and light. There was a green belt of shrubbery every few hundred yards, making the estate resemble even more a child's model of a village. It was the brain child of a statistician bodied forth into bricks and mortar, lying like a Procrustean trap for the Black Rowites, who, if they lacked practically everything else, certainly had individuality in dollops.

Father put his finger on the first flaw. Each house had been allocated a little strip of garden in front, but the soil was a wasted mass of rubble. Father was indignant.

'Do they expect folks to grow owt on that?' he grumbled, then reacted with characteristic cunning.

He borrowed a wheelbarrow from Old Nick, the farmer, and carefully dug off the surface soil of our old garden. Then he and Fred, who had been loaned by Sadie for the occasion, wheeled load upon load to the cree which had formerly housed our few hens, and when it was full they padlocked the shed to keep out marauders. The door of our house was never locked, because it contained nothing worth pinching.

Shifting day arrived and Nicholson's horse and cart were pressed into service to convey our furniture to our new dwelling-to-be. Everybody in the family carried parcels of oddments, making repeated treks to denude the old home first of its possessions and finally of its atmosphere. While the adults were busy arranging things to their liking and discovering uneasily that everything we had looked shabby and incongruous in the small paperless rooms, I slipped off to retrieve Nipper, our cat of the period.

I remember holding the furry black body in my arms to quieten its beating heart, as I drifted through the shrunken rooms which, stripped of all pretensions, already seemed unfamiliar and hostile. The warmth of living had gone from the old house and it was dying with the peace that comes at the end of a long life of hard work.

I wandered outside to take my farewell of the ruined garden, stepping unchecked through the once-cherished rosebed, then I squatted beside the cree that had belonged to Ted, breathing in the tarry smell, stroking the cat, and thinking of nothing. Idly I pricked blebs of tar bubbles from the wooden slats, lost in a hiatus in time.

Sounds of activity made me look up. Father was coming along from the farm, with Percy in tow.

'What?' yelled the farmer's son outraged. 'Me shift muck? I'm not a bleddy midden man. No fear.'

Father cast his eyes skywards in despair, hobbling along to keep up with Percy's big strides.

'Call yourself a shifting expert?' he taunted. 'Thoo knows nowt about it. Thoo cannot shift theself off thy own backside.'

Percy stopped dead, laying his big meaty hands on his corduroys.

'I know this much,' he said with spirit. 'I'll not take impitence from you much longer. I'll be glad to see the back of you.'

You could only go so far with Percy, then you had to use tact. Father used to say that Percy put him in mind of an old cuddy his family had at Avelstan. Every time it had to haul a load of water up the bank, it stopped dead outside Father's pub. Nothing would make it move on except a sup of beer, which it regarded as a rightful reward for its labour. Thinking of the cuddy, Father changed his tactics with Percy.

'Eeh now, Porcy, lad,' he said in his mild 'genuine' voice, 'I nivor thowt the day would come when owld Bob Nicholson's bairn would speak to me in that tone of voice.'

He leant over his stick, cunningly bending his shoulders, then went on in a hesitant voice thick with country overtones.

'Why man, me and your father has known one another for many a year. I mind when you were born. Your father was ower the moon. Fancy—'

Percy couldn't bear to hear any more in this strain. Although there was no perceptible change of expression on his face – for it was so red and heavy with stupidity that any emotion had to struggle through layers of flesh before it could register – yet his voice was apologetic when he answered.

'Say no more aboot it. I'll shift the muck for ye.'

Father's recovery was so instantaneous that even Percy must have suspected that he'd been manipulated.

'That's Bob's lad talking,' he said heartily, laughing delightedly. 'And when I win first prize at the show, I'll stand you a drink, Porcy.'

Percy grunted with derisory disbelief, but set to willingly enough to cart Father's precious soil down to the new garden.

Father's euphoria saddened me. Still holding the cat I crept away without a backward glance at Ted's old cree and wandered broodily over the debris where Teasdale's wooden house had stood till the Coöncil had decreed otherwise. Authority was ordering everybody's life now – even Porcy's. He wasn't even allowed to overcome the temptation to dilute the milk now. Every morning he had to drive his milk-cart along to the Co-op dairy, where 'they' relieved him of his load of milk, tested it, sterilized it and put it into nice clean bottles, each containing exactly a pint.

I sighed and idly kicked at a flapping piece of peeled-off wallpaper. I recognized the flamboyant pattern and grinned a little as I thought of Mrs. Teasdale who had fetched it back from the Stores so proudly, then invited in all the neighbours to admire it. In a way Mrs. Teasdale was a true altruist – she didn't do anything without thinking of the effect it was going to have on others. She thrived on envy, but her attempts to rouse it were so painfully naïve that she misfired every time and only caused amusement. She was indulged by the Rowites as a genuine caricature who deceived no one but herself.

Mr. Teasdale had a responsible position in the Co-op grocery department – according to his wife. In actual fact, he went round with the Store cart, delivering grocery orders. His 'responsibility' may have extended to seeing that the horse had enough to eat, but that was its limit. Nevertheless Mrs. Teasdale, by virtue of her husband's position, considered herself a cut above the miners and other 'manual workers'.

During the strike she had endeared herself to the Black Rowites by standing outside her scullery door, like a come-on man at a fair, shouting for her son to come in for his dinner. At a time when the rest of us considered ourselves lucky to get a slice of bread and dripping, she would yell, 'Walter, *Wal*-ter. Come in and get your meat and potatoes and cabbage and gravy before they get cold.'

Eventually a group of us children would collect round the lamp-post and helpfully join in the refrain.

'Walter,' we would yell. 'Come and get your meat and potatoes and cabbage and gravy and pepper and salt and mustard and worms and caterpillars and maggots . . .'

We'd continue the list derisively until Mrs. Teasdale flounced in-doors, Walterless. That would teach her to boast in front of us strikers' kids!

Now as my foot toyed with the flapping fragment of wallpaper, I'd have given anything to have the old times back. At twelve I was already nostalgic for the lost freedom of my youth, but I had the sense to turn my back on its memory and plod off purposefully to the new house, with its aggressive smell of paint and putty.

All the furniture had been piled outside the back door, taking up every inch of space in the walled-in back garden we'd been allocated. Mother was struggling with the wash hand-stand, but the ornate Victorian monstrosity wouldn't go through the doorway. Feeling in the way, I squeezed past and went indoors, my feet clanking out raw echoes on the new wooden floorboards.

The carved glass-fronted 'press', pride of our old kitchen, was tucked away ignominiously under the stairs. The bottom half of our side-board stood uneasily in the poky living-room, but the top half, with its huge mirror and intricately curved curlicues, lay rejected on the stairs, weighed and found wanting.

All of us buckled to. We heaved and pushed and carried until eventually we'd succeeded in capturing most of our furniture in the red-brick trap, but the wash-stand refused to enter. It stood at bay in the back-yard, contemptuously indifferent to our kicks and pushes. Thwarted, we meanly threatened to cut off its legs, but it seemed to know that it had us beaten. Uncompromisingly Victorian to the end, it escaped us.

We all spoke in whispers that first day in the new house, as if afraid of betraying ourselves before strangers. Indeed the whole of the estate seemed immolated. The hearty gusto of yore might never have been. All the tenants were on their best behaviour, making cautious overtures to the hot and cold taps and tiptoeing apologetically upstairs in a vague attempt to placate the watching lares and penates. We had all, with awe, discovered privacy, even though we shared the front path with our next-door neighbours.

Next morning, in the back-yard, Father and Mother surveyed the wash-stand.

'D'ye mind when we got that thing, Jennie?'

'I do that, Joe. It was a wedding present from Aunt Maggie.'

Mother blushed and giggled as Father rolled his eyes at her.

'She never liked me, thon,' he admitted, then added more boldly, 'and I never liked that wash-stand. We've had it ower thirty years, and every time I've looked at it, it's put me in mind of Aunt Maggie. And it's given me many a nasty jab on the ankle, forby.'

Mother looked down her nose at the admission, then said in a rush of confidence: 'I never washed that marble top without thinking of poor old Uncle Jed lying there without a tombstone.'

'Aye,' Father agreed. 'She was a mean old beggar, was Aunt Maggie.'

He looked speculatively at the mottled marble top.

'It *would* have made a nice headstone at that, Jennie,' he conceded.

They exchanged a sly look of complicity, then Father had an idea.

'What aboot letting Porcy have it?' he suggested. 'It's no more use tiv us, and it's just the sort of thing he would like.'

Now that she'd broken the rule about looking gift-horses in the mouth, Mother didn't even make a show of resistance.

'I'm sick of the sight of the big ugly thing,' she said briskly. 'I'll be glad to get shot of it.'

So it was arranged. That afternoon Percy fetched his last load of soil down from the cree and helped Father to spread it. We all helped to clear away stones and rubble to make way for the good black soil and we all caught some of Father's infectious enthusiasm for the task.

'There now,' said Father at length, straightening his back. 'Thoo's done a good job there, Porcy. And we'll not forget it.'

Expansively he led the farmer's son through the house and into the back enclosure where the wash-stand stood.

'What d'ye think of that?' he demanded, then seeing Percy's sour expression, went on hastily. 'The wife wants yer to have a keepsake, Porcy, so load thon wash-stand on thy cart and had away off with it.'

As soon as he saw that he wasn't expected to buy it, Percy's attitude changed and he worked quickly before Father changed his mind. We all stood at the back gate and watched Percy drive off with his reward, for which he'd given no thanks.

'I hope it jabs *his* ankle,' muttered Father, then he caught sight of something.

'Had away and fetch a pail and shovel, lass,' he told me. 'It's not often Porcy gives summat away for nowt, but his horse has left us a tip this time.'

So I shovelled the horse droppings into a bucket and carried them off to the bottom of the new garden to mark the beginning of a new compost heap. With care Father selected the site for his new leek-bed – nearer the gate this time, the better to be seen by his cronies.

The new house was beginning to seem more like home, but there was still something wrong with the estate. For about a week there was this feeling of the alien, then I heard something that put my mind at rest. From the yard at the end of our block I heard a voice that, though raucous, was like music to my ears. The spirit of the Black Rows was stirring from slumber.

Timidly at first, then unashamedly crowing came the voice of Mrs. Teasdale.

'Walter – *Wal*-ter! Come and get your peas and potatoes and mutton and gravy.'

I sighed happily. All was well.

10. Marriage

THE curiosity I felt towards affairs of the flesh, unslaked by the evasive approach of the confirmation classes, flourished during my fourteenth year. Jane, out of a sense of duty, prepared me for Life by acquainting me with the facts about reproduction on one of our rare Sunday morning walks. The theory I understood, but the emotional effect on people seemed to me to be rather excessive. I became interested in studying married couples.

Mother had to withstand some curious appraisals, but nothing would put her out of countenance. I'd probably have accepted 'seck' as part of the natural scheme of things, if a trifle overrated, had I not come into contact with its devastating effects at about the same time as I discovered its functions. I already connected it vaguely with marriage.

Shortly after we went on the Means Test, Fred had left home to become Sadie Pratt's husband. He didn't do anything so definite as decide to marry her. Sadie made all the decisions even during their meagre courtship. Looking back on the affair now, I suppose their decision to marry sprang from their youthful revolt against possessive families and frustrating conditions – it may have been an exciting challenge to fate.

From the way the news was received at home, I got the impression that marriage was not only selfish, it was wicked. Instead of acting as a son should, Fred shelved his responsibilities and acted like an ungrateful cur. Sadie, his chosen mate, was a forthright young woman with strong arms, a strong will and a sharp tongue. Father would have taken an instinctive dislike to her even if she hadn't 'hooked' our Fred. As it was, her snatching the breadwinner from our midst, before we'd had any good of his earnings, was *the* cardinal crime. From the beginning, Father conducted against Sadie a feud that was as slyly delightful as it was unfair.

Partly because we were on the Means Test and unable to make a splash, and partly because Fred was leaving us all in the lurch, the wedding was a hole-and-corner affair. The ceremony took place in the chapel, without music or gaiety. Sadie marched up the aisle with a determined look on her long face and grasped Fred's arm in a predatory way, at once claiming him and protecting him from slights. Mrs. Pratt put on some sort of a meal after the brief ceremony, but none of our family, except Alice, attended. Jane naturally couldn't make a special trip home for the wedding, and Sadie, tight-lipped, regarded her absence as a declaration of war.

Mother couldn't afford to buy a present, but she'd done the decent thing and dived into the big wooden box that was kept in the middle room, to emerge with an old but good linen tablecloth. This she'd presented to Fred in silence, not being able to face Sadie's impudent triumph.

She may eventually have come to accept Sadie as a daughter-in-law, may even have appreciated her sterling worth, for Sadie was hewn out of the granite that makes a good pitman's wife, but the relationship started off on the wrong footing and never recovered.

Sadie chose to be insulted by Mother's gift.

'Does she think I'm not good enough for her?' she asked Fred in a fury. 'Giving me mouldy old cast-offs. You can tell her to keep her family heirlooms.'

Her heavy features flushed an unattractive red and she flung the offending tablecloth into a corner. At that moment she looked as dangerous as a man and Fred's momentary flicker of weakness conditioned his entire relationship with Sadie ever afterwards. Instead of giving her a good clout across the jaw for her spiteful display of temper, he let her see that he was beaten. Quietly he walked over to the corner and picked up the cloth. In that moment, Sadie became a shrew. She needed a firm hand to control her fine strength and intense loyalty. Properly handled, she'd have been all that Fred hoped for when he first saw the raw-boned girl with the bold eyes. It was a moment of mutual disillusion. Sadie, thinking that Fred's manliness was a façade concealing contemptible weakness, turned her strength against him and battered away at his confidence to earn a cheap and bitter triumph. She'd been cheated, and she rationalized her frustration into a hatred of Jane and my parents.

Mother, unwittingly, played into Sadie's hands. Hurt at Fred's desertion, but much too proud to show it, she ignored Sadie's existence at first. This was Mother's way of coming to terms with disagreeable realities, and in time she'd have accepted Sadie and made the best of things. Reinforcing her assumed indifference was her natural shyness, her dislike of demonstrative behaviour. This coolness, Sadie chose to interpret as stand-offishness. Their relationship never recovered from this initial bitterness and hardened into a real antipathy.

Father, with characteristic bluntness, was prejudiced against Sadie from the start. He never had a good word to say for her. He objected to her full lips – 'mouth like a letterbox', her independent spirit – 'always on the look out for mischief, thon', even her voice – 'like a gramophone needle that's got stuck'. He had the eye of a caricaturist and it is doubtful if the rest of us ever saw the real Sadie, her image overlaid as it was by Father's cruelly exaggerating outline. From the beginning we all regarded her as impossible, a 'hard nut, that one'.

Not unnaturally, Sadie retaliated. Loyalty to Fred took the form of a grudge against Jane, the privileged. (It is always more flattering to transmute one's jealousies into a fight for justice for the underdog.) Sadie's remarks had a habit of being repeated to Father, whose spies were everywhere.

'Fred never had a chance,' she had declared. 'Their Jane got everything that was going. If it hadn't been for Fred working down the pit to help out, she'd never have got through college. He was *sacrificed* for that stuck-up Jane.'

Pettier remarks, aimed at Mother's efforts to make ends meet, were equally hurtful and not so funny.

'It's no good offering Fred mutton,' she'd say with a smirk. 'He had to eat so much scrag-end at home that he's ashamed to look a sheep in the face.'

We all considered that a blow beneath the belt. Fred's visits home, always rare, became increasingly uncomfortable until they stopped altogether.

'That bitch with the big mouth,' declared Father with bitter triumph, 'has turned our Fred against his own family. She won't even let him come and see his own folks.'

Ted, Alice and I were suitably awed.

'Mind you,' he'd admonish the three of us, 'I want none of you bairns to gang alang there. Let them stew in their own juice.'

Impressed, we'd nod solemnly. Like an amoeba ejecting waste material, the family spewed out Fred, then closed up again, tighter.

I was beginning to see marriage as a form of betrayal to the family. Shortly after my fourteenth birthday, I saw it as something worse. Marriage, I realized with a shock, wasn't a static state. It could change and develop in unpleasant ways.

During the summer holidays, Jane took me with her to visit Hettie, our flapper cousin who'd married the Appleby boy and gone off with him to the East Midlands six years before. They'd never been back up north for a visit even when their sons and daughter were born, so Jane's visit was a cause for excitement. Her decision to take me with her was partly utilitarian and partly as a form of insurance – almost a talisman.

Apart from Sunday School trips to the coast for a day, and an occasional jaunt to 'the toon', I had never been away from Rainton so I was thrilled at the idea of enlarging my horizons. We were going to spend over three hours in the train – adventure unlimited!

Jane's enthusiasm was tempered with a superstitious caution. Natural curiosity and the nostalgic memory of her friendship with Hettie struggled with a prophetic uneasiness at what lay in store for her. For Jane was going to the East Midland village in answer to Hettie's appeal. A fourth child was expected and Hettie couldn't cope. Jane was to help her over the confinement and stay for the christening. What caused the frown to pucker Jane's brow was not her new responsibility, but Hettie's comments on the married state. How much of this despair was caused by Hettie's physical state and how much by disillusion, Jane was anxious to discover.

According to Hettie's rather incoherent letter, there was no gilt left on her marriage, and precious little gingerbread. The very qualities which had dazzled her in Bert as a lover, had proved impossible in a husband. Bert's gaiety had been too closely related to the bottle, his recklessness contained more than a touch of brutality, his once attractive air of insouciance sprang from a stupid insensitivity. Bert was shiftless and lazy.

After the windfall from his mother had been frittered away, Bert

drifted into the shiftless existence of casual labourer. He was allergic to
work. Hettie was soon overwhelmed by the claims of a small family
and her fourth pregnancy was proving unexpectedly difficult. It wasn't
so much the catalogue of misfortunes or the defeatist tone of the letter
that had prompted Jane to accept Hettie's invitation – it was the naïve
appeal in the scrawled post-script. 'For old times sake.' Jane was in the
train bound for the Midlands with me tagging along as a necessity
whose function was as yet undefined. But Jane hadn't forgotten the
wedding day.

There was no one to meet us at the station. We had arrived at
Wrexham, a little market town just over the Lincolnshire border. It
was late afternoon as we made our laden way to the bus station, where
we learnt that there were only two buses a week to Larton, our
destination.

Jane and I sat in the deserted bus shelter, clutching our cases and
brown-paper parcels. Jane looked worried but I was excited. I
liked the open country faces of the Wrexham people; I liked the queer
old buildings round the square, and I was fascinated by the slow burr of
the local dialect. Wrexham was what my father would have called 'a
sedate little place'. My spirits soared.

To cheer Jane up, and to reinforce my exhilarating sense of difference,
I sang snatches of a local North Country song.

> 'Noo when we got to Rowlands Gill
> The morning train had gone –
> The porter says there was nee more
> Till twenty minutes to one.
>> Wor Nan's a mazer and a mazer she'll remain
>> As lang as I live I'll nivor for-*get* the day we missed the train.'

That was the most cheerful part of our visit.

Bert arrived, grinning with beery affability.

'I wondered where you'd got to,' he said, swaying towards us.

Jane grimly picked up her case, which Bert hadn't offered to take.

'I might have known where *you'd* got to,' she muttered as we
stumbled after him across the square to a rickety old cart.

Bert slapped the tired-looking pony on the neck.

'What do you think of it?' he asked proudly.

Jane looked at the broken-down cart, the shambling old pony, then
at Bert. He had the same old insolent arrogance, but he'd lost the cause
of it. His unshaven chin no longer looked disturbingly masculine – it

looked furtive. His ingratiating grin exposed the blackened stumps of neglected teeth. His careless disregard of dress had degenerated into a disgusting sloppiness. He looked like a disreputable tramp, slimy with moral decay.

Jane's silent scrutiny made Bert uneasy. His nasty temper, never far from the surface, bubbled up to gain vicious expression in a shambling kick at the pony's foreleg.

'Where did you pick that thing up?' asked Jane icily.

Bert flashed her a look from bloodshot eyes. His fuddled brain seemed to detect her marked lack of admiration. Then his frown vanished and he laughed suggestively.

'Still got plenty of spirit, eh?' nudging her. He swaggered in a parody of masculine supremacy. 'What *you* need's a man to keep you in order, girl.'

Jane stepped back and grabbed my arm.

'We'll wait for the bus. You go by yourself.'

Bert's voice rose to a roar.

'You won't get no bloody bus. It's gone, d'ye see? You'll come along with me, the pair of yer or ye can turn yourselves roond and get the next train back to bloody Rainton. Understand?'

To avoid a scene, Jane climbed into the cart. I was yanked off my feet and plonked beside her, then Bert got up himself. We were joggled along at a dangerous pace past rows of fields where poppies bloomed bright among the corn, then we reached the 'settlement' – a row of labourers' cottages. One of these was Bert's.

'I'm me own boss now,' he'd told us on the cart. 'I've got a bit of land and a few hens and pigs, and I make a bit on the side with me horse and cart.'

It sounded enviable, and might have been had Bert been only half a man. Jane held my hand tightly, making no comment, except to give it a squeeze when the 'cottage' came into view, as if sharing my disappointment. My preconceived notion of country life in picturesque cottages, based on highly coloured calendars, collapsed like a burst balloon. I knew a slum when I saw one.

'Woman,' yelled Bert, stalking into the house. 'Stir yourself. They've come.'

We stepped down into a narrow little room, blinking to accustom our eyes to the flickering oil lamp our noses had already detected. From a low archway opposite the fireplace, Hettie appeared. Even in this light the change in her was startling.

She was stick thin, apart from the swollen belly that was barely covered by a huge sack apron. Her hair was lank and tatty, and the bones stuck out from her face. What chilled me more than her appearance was the way her eyes went straight to her husband's face before she looked at her guests. As if gaining his permission, she held out her calloused hands towards Jane.

'So you've come.' Her voice sounded thin as well, as if you could break it.

Bert, who had flung off the unaccustomed jacket, apparently thought that enough time had been allocated for sentimental reunions and set himself the task of showing us who was boss.

'I want a cup of tea. Make sharp. Look at the time.'

Obediently Hettie turned back towards the archway, but Jane intervened. 'Sit yourself down, Hettie. I'll make it.'

She'd reckoned without Bert, who casually stretched out a long leg. 'Hettie's all right. She's not made of glass, are you, lass?'

At his glance, Hettie became sprightly, simpering in grotesque parody of the flighty young girl she'd once been. The laugh she'd developed in imitation of Bert, had weakened to a nervous snigger, but it still had the same knowing sound.

'You might teach bairns their alphabets,' she said to Jane with painful archness, one hand on her huge apron, 'but I know more about men folks. I'll make Bert his tea the way he likes it.'

Bert's appreciative guffaw might have been given to a dog that had successfully performed a trick for visitors. With a red face Jane looked round the room, taking in the broken door on the sideboard, the holes in the oilcloth, the ingrained stains on the tablecloth, then she raised her head and looked straight at Bert as he lolled back in the creaking armchair with his legs straddled across the fender. The light of Rechabite zeal was in her eyes.

'I'll give her a hand all the same,' she said quietly.

I went after her into the kitchen, a surprisingly big room with stone flags on the floor. Two of the children were squabbling under the table.

Jane went straight over to the corner where the baby was crying in its pram. She picked it up gingerly, wiped its mouth, rearranged its blankets, then went to wash her hands at the sink. I could see from the set of her shoulders that she wouldn't eat a thing in that house until she'd cleared away the coat of grime that lay over everything in it. Still wearing the hat and coat she'd travelled in, Jane filled the huge iron pan with cold water and set it on the fire. The fact that there was no hot-water system in the house acted on her like a challenge. I had never been prouder of my sister.

For the next two weeks, while Hettie lay in bed, Jane and I scrubbed and polished and washed and ironed. The kitchen was always full of steam from the big iron pan, which Jane regarded almost ritualistically as a defence against sloth as well as dirt. When she attempted to serve the potatoes in a tureen, Bert laughed at her daintiness.

'This is good enough for us,' he shouted, emptying the potatoes back into the boiling pan. 'We like to dive in and help ourselves.'

One afternoon when we had the place to ourselves, Jane baked an enormous batch of scones to stave off the perpetual hunger of the Appleby family.

'You would think,' she said, tight-lipped, as she fastened the lid on the huge tin box, 'they'd never had a meal in their lives. They've got enough to eat, but half the stuff is wasted. Hettie's no manager.'

Then she took me off for a walk. The countryside was flat, the air warm and sticky, smelling headily of fresh hay. The earth had a heavy reddish quality which I found oppressive as if it hindered my breathing.

'Poor Mary,' said my sister, touching my shoulder. 'It's not much of a holiday for you, trying to keep those brats occupied.'

Then she held up her coarsened hands in horror.

'I wouldn't mind,' she said with a fierceness that might have indicated to someone more experienced than I the strain she was undergoing, 'if your efforts were only appreciated. But Hettie's just as bad as Bert now. Lazy – shiftless – she's turned into a proper slut. And a whiner. Always on the cadge.'

I nodded importantly. I'd never felt closer to Jane.

'Did you see that photograph on the mantelpiece?'

Jane sighed. It was the one we had in our album.

'Yes. She doesn't look much like that now, does she?'

We walked on in silence, our feet clamping on the rough track. I caught my breath as a dragonfly whizzed past in a dizzy whirl of translucent colours. Jane didn't even notice it. Her eyes had a strained inward look. She was searching for the Hettie she'd known – and perhaps the Jane too.

'If only she *knew* what's happened to her,' she went on in a bewildered tone. 'But she thinks I'm the one that's changed. She calls me *fussy.*'

We reached the cross-roads then turned and reluctantly retraced our steps.

'I liked Wrexham,' I said impulsively. 'Jane – can we go there tomorrow – just you and me? It's the bus day.'

Jane looked tempted, then shook her head. 'I can't leave Hetty that long. Never mind, Mary. It won't be long now.'

We arrived at the 'cottage' to find that Bert had unearthed the tin of fresh scones and had wolfed most of them. The children had finished them off. A flash of anger transformed Jane. A termagant dashed into the bedroom where Hettie lay and chokingly demanded a show-down.

'Hettie. Did you know about this?' Jane held out the empty tin.

An unpleasant flush stained Hettie's sharpened features. '*I* didn't have any,' she whined, then turned resentful. 'They were made to be eaten, weren't they?'

Jane looked at her, then her shoulders slumped. What was the good? I hadn't realized until then how strained Jane was. It was as though the scream of protest she'd bottled up inside her since our arrival had voiced itself. Now she was ashamed of her lack of control.

'Yes,' she said woodenly. 'Yes, they were.'

In the kitchen the children, encouraged by Bert, were creating chaos. They'd sensed the defeat of Jane, whose strangeness and authority had quietened them before, and now they let their natural spirits rip. Bert sprawled in the middle of it, letting the children crawl all over him. To add to the din, the mangy old dog yelped hysterically, foraging for bits of discarded scones.

Bert was an unpredictable father. Sometimes he'd be maudlin and demonstrative, letting the children scramble for a handful of coppers, or ticing them to have a sup of beer. At other times he'd boot them out of his way with a curse, fingering at his belt threateningly.

Andy, who was six, was both terrified of his father and obsessively attached to his mother although Hettie was remarkably indifferent to the boy, jeering at him for being a baby. Once I had to fetch him in for his tea. After a long search I found him at the top of the garden, punching a sack of hen-feed with his puny fists. I didn't laugh when I caught sight of the oddly mature look of concentration on his childish features. Whether he wanted to become manly to gain his mother's respect, or to become tough enough to knock his father down, I couldn't guess, but the sight disturbed me.

When the new baby arrived, Bert was out at the pub as usual, and I had to go for the midwife. Jane and the old woman were shut up in the big bedroom for ages while I kept an eye on the sleeping children, eventually falling asleep myself. Next day, Jane let me tiptoe in and look at Hettie and her baby.

Hettie's hands were so white that you could nearly see through them and her face looked rested and almost pretty. But I had eyes only for the baby, which seemed like an unopened rhubarb leaf, all curled up, waiting for nourishment to help it to push itself out of its folds. Jane's expression was wonderfully gentle as she looked at it. For it was to this end that all her efforts had been directed. She and Hettie seemed to be linked as they never had before.

Hettie stayed in bed for a week, during which Jane had complete charge of the household. She had an easy, relaxed manner and had it not been for Bert, would have been content. But with Hettie unavailable and absorbed in the new baby, Bert's masculinity became rampant. He adopted an unpleasantly familiar tone towards Jane, who at first mistook it for friendliness. Then he started giving her affectionate but painful slaps on the buttocks when she had to squeeze past him.

Once he even brought tears to her eyes. He'd offered her a drink to 'wet the baby's head', and when Jane refused, he grasped her arm, squeezing it painfully. He had a bit of strength in those blackened fingers. Jane stood perfectly still, biting her lip hard to avoid giving him the satisfaction of seeing that he'd hurt her. Bert brought his face very close to hers and spoke in a caressing voice.

'You'll have a drop to please me. Won't you, Jane?'

Jane stared at his face fascinated, as if she'd never seen him before, looking at the moist red lips so close to hers. Then she shivered and jerked herself out of his slackened grip, taking him off guard. Bert, surprised, let his mouth drop open foolishly, then he laughed softly, as if pleased.

'So that's the way of it, is it?' he said in a crooning voice he'd never used before.

Jane didn't reply. She was breathing quickly as if she'd been stunned by a revelation. After that she took care never to let me out of her sight. She ignored Bert completely, lowering her eyes when she had to speak to him, being excessively polite. Bert didn't seem annoyed, but when she was in the room his eyes never left her. An undercurrent of tension gradually built up between them.

Every night, Jane counted the days until it would be safe to leave Hettie, who was making a slow recovery. She lay in bed with the baby in the crook of her arm, enjoying her unaccustomed idleness, thinking up exotic names for her daughter.

A week before Jane was due back at school, the baby was christened – Penelope Jane. For the ceremony Hettie wore one of Jane's dresses, and when she was dressed to her satisfaction, the three grown ups went off to the church leaving me in charge of the children. Bert, looking unaccustomedly spruce, towered above the two cousins, holding each by her elbow.

Hettie was eager and excited by this attention, casting proud peeps at Jane, who was stiffly unresponsive. Bert was very quiet but his lips kept twitching as if he were amused, like a child gaining secret satisfaction out of pretending to conform to adult patterns of behaviour.

I opened the door to them on their return. Hettie proudly showed me the baby, who had been as good as gold at the ceremony. She was incredibly tiny and perfect in every detail, lying unsmilingly among the folds of the shawl, her doll-like face covered by the christening veil. I was struck by her marble immobility.

Before I could stop myself, the words came out. 'She looks like a little corpse, laid out like that.'

The effect of my thoughtless words on Hettie was startling. She almost spat at me.

'You'll bring bad luck on us,' she moaned, looking cross-eyed in her intensity. 'What a thing to say. What possessed you to say a thing like that?'

She looked to Bert for confirmation of her attitude, but he was leaning against the doorpost, hands in pockets, his eyes on Jane who was removing her hat and coat. Hettie stood holding the baby towards him with stiff arms, as if she'd forgotten what she was doing. Nobody moved for a moment, then suddenly all was activity.

'Get the glasses out, woman,' Bert told her. 'I feel like a bit of a do.'

Some of the neighbours popped in to see the baby and stayed to drink its health. Jane handed out glasses of beer to disguise her own abstinence and to avoid their frank appraising stares. In no time the air in the little parlour was heavy with smoke and the powerful smell of hops. The baby lay on the couch forgotten for the moment, still in its christening robes, moving its tiny hands in ineffectual jerks against the constricting lace, splendidly impervious to the clink of glasses and the shouts of coarse laughter.

The dog, privileged for once, prepared to jump on to the couch beside the baby, but Jane, seeing its intention, dashed over to prevent it.

Bert put out his long arm and grasped her round the waist. He'd taken off his jacket and loosened his shirt, and the beer was rising in him.

'Stay there, lass,' he told Jane. 'I'll fettle that beast.' And with a powerful lunge he dislodged the dog and sent it cowering into a corner.

He turned to Jane with an insolent grin, parading his power.

'*He* knows who's master here.'

Without a word Jane collected me and took me straight out of the house along the familiar path to the cross-roads, the boundary of our freedom. A light drizzle was blurring the outline of the hedges, settling in tiny drops on Jane's uncovered hair, giving her a faery look. Uncaring, she breathed in the moist air in huge gulps, as if to wash away the image of the baby in that room. Her eyes were moist, whether with tears or rain I couldn't tell.

'We're going tomorrow,' she said flatly. 'First thing.'

We turned and looked at the group of cottages with their soft yellow lights gleaming invitingly at this remove.

'We've done the best we can,' she went on. 'But it's had no effect. They're too set in their warp.'

I struggled, groping towards an attitude.

'Is this what it's like when you get married, Jane?'

'You've seen for yourself.' Bitterness made her voice curt. 'Men are just a lot of animals.'

Something drained away from me – perhaps a belief in the fairy tale ending of 'happy ever after'. I shivered. Slowly we walked back, our arms round each other's waists, then paused at the gate, listening to the bursts of laughter and voices raised in argument. Neither of us wanted to go back.

'Slip straight upstairs,' Jane told me. 'And start packing. Our work here is finished.'

That night I lay awake, wishing that Jane didn't have to go back to digs. I wanted her to be at home with me, to make me feel safe. Rainton might be dull and gloomy, but it was different from the outside world. Cleaner, despite its coal muck. I suddenly felt homesick.

·   ·   ·   ·   ·

'Your holiday doesn't seem to have done you much good,' Mother stated impatiently.

Since my return I'd been moony and lethargic. Everything seemed pointless. If I remained inactive I had a superstitious hope that life would become solider, more stable. Mother, an active woman, turned sceptical eyes on my laziness.

'A young girl like you should be getting the benefit of some fresh air,' she went on at me.

To escape her searching eyes, I started going to the Carnegie library and spending hours in the reading-room, which was musty with the smell of eternity. What began as a therapy developed into an interest. I read voraciously. I not only read, I studied the librarian, John Willy Dobson, a local 'character'.

Nobody ever referred to him as Mr. Dobson, although he was punctilious for dignity. He was a brisk little man, always dashing in and out of rooms rubbing his hands and reminding borrowers of the rules of the library which had been drawn up by John Willy in person.

He was a terror for discipline. Sneeze in his presence and he'd haul you in front of his huge placard where SILENCE was inscribed in huge gothic letters. For John Willy's only talent was calligraphy. With loving care he inscribed his beloved rules in Indian ink on impeccable squares of paper which he stuck up all over the library. He was forever re-sorting the books so that he could stick fresh little labels all over the non-fiction sections. It was impossible to find a book in Rainton library. A volume on the Great War began as History, graduated through Europe, Science and Miscellaneous and finished up under Fine Arts.

He was affable and unctuous to borrowers, and he'd been known to waive a fine if you took out a book he recommended, but if he detected a finger-mark or a dog-eared cover in a returned book, he'd go beserk. Out would come his enormous rubber and he'd cluck and tutter at you in a frenzy. For books were John Willy's children.

There was some mystery in John Willy's life. When his name cropped up in conversation, people would pause and shake their heads, murmur 'Poor John Willy', and talk animatedly about something else. There was laughter, pity and deference all mixed up in their attitude to the man, and this complexity caused them to hold him in a curious reverence.

For once Father was not communicative.

'What makes John Willy so queer?' I asked him.

' Queer? How do you mean, queer?'

It was not like Father to temporize.

'The pompous way he laughs,' I offered vaguely. 'The way he flies off the handle at the least bit thing. *You* know—'

It was difficult to define, but the queerness was so solid that you could cut it with a knife.

'Well now, he's always been a fussy little body,' Father conceded. 'But there's nowt wrong with that. Nowt that you might call *queer*.'

'Have you known him long?' I was impatient with this hedging.

'All his life. And his father afore him.'

'And he's always been like this?' I neatly sidestepped an incursion into local genealogy.

'Aye, he always was a bit eccentric.' Father chuckled remembering. 'It was funny how he came to get that job, years ago. There was three of them in for it. The other two was fine upstanding men, mark you – eddicated men at that, but John Willy got the job.'

'Wasn't he educated?'

Father leant forward and looked at me, impressively.

'Have you ever seen John Willy *read* one of them books in the library?'

I was shocked. 'Do you mean he can't *read*?'

'I'm not saying he cannot *now*,' answered Father cryptically. 'I'm talking aboot *then*. Thirty years ago.'

'But how did he get the librarian's job if he couldn't read?'

As usual I was torn between frank disbelief and a temptation to accept Father's fantasy as truth.

'As far as I remember,' he reminisced, 'the committee couldn't make up their minds at the interview. So they decided to give all three candidates a test.'

'What sort of test?'

'They all had to copy out a page of this book. And John Willy won. He has a lovely copperplate hand.'

The explanation was plausible, but I couldn't accept it. I brooded while Father shook his head.

'You've got to be kind to poor John Willy,' he told me. 'He's turned a bit eccentric after what he's been through. And you canna blame him.'

No more was forthcoming after this neat evasion. My curiosity burned. I took to watching John Willy dash about the library clicking his tongue, and I'd wonder. To satisfy my curiosity I even questioned the assistant librarian, a pimply youth with dirty finger-nails and lank fair hair. He was voluble.

'Everything I do is wrong,' he whined, looking nervously over his shoulder. 'I'm on my blessed feet all day long and John Willy trails after me, doing all my work again – *his* way. And because *he* stays behind every evening in the office, he expects everybody else to. What he finds to do there, *I* don't know.'

Maybe he read secretly, I thought. I pictured John Willy painfully stumbling through a child's primer, then dismissed the fantasy. Perhaps he drew up grandiose plans for the lectures he kept arranging, despite the fact that hardly anybody ever attended. The possibilities were endless.

One evening, after the library had closed, I was coming back from the doctor's and I noticed the light from the office window gleaming like an iridescent sprite in the darkened building. I hesitated, because the library looked sullen and threatening in the flickering glow of the street lamp, then I made up my mind and walked purposefully to the side door, knocking before my resolution failed. I nearly ran away at that point, but I heard John Willy's familiar skip, then the door opened.

There was a peculiar expression on his face, a look of avid eagerness, pitiful in so comic a figure. It was only a momentary flicker, then the old John Willy was back, the buruaocrat outraged at my interruption.

'What do you want here at this time of night? The library's closed.'

His finger groped automatically for a notice.

I stammered something about needing a book for an essay, but John Willy was adamant. Rules were not to be broken. If there had been an accident outside the library door I doubt whether he'd loan the witnesses a book on First Aid, if it happened after closing hours. He shut the door firmly in my face and I walked thoughtfully home, to seek out Father.

I told him of my fruitless visit and he nodded sagely.

'I might have known you wouldn't be satisfied until you'd found out. You've got to get to the far end of everything.'

He smiled fleetingly. I was his own daughter right enough.

'But you must have given John Willy an awful fright, hinny. In the circumstances it was the worst thing ye could have done.'

Then he told me. John Willy's young wife had left him shortly after he got the librarianship. The shock had unsettled him. The library had become his whole life – his wife, the children he never had – almost his religion. He paid off the house and kept it spick and span, in readiness for his wife's return. Nobody was ever invited inside that house, and nobody ever should be, until its mistress took charge of it.

A disturbing thought occurred to me.

'Da – when he opened the side door of the library tonight – did he think it was her?'

'Aye, very likely,' agreed Father. 'You see, lass, he remembers her as she was thirty years ago – just a slip of a girl. She'd look a bonny sight different now, if ever she *did* turn up again.'

The story made a deep impression on me. I had to reconsider my views on marriage. Perhaps Jane was biased – perhaps it wasn't all squalid, like Hettie's marriage had become. In my imagination John Willy became a compound of all the virtues – a romantic figure, faithful to an ideal – in fact, a very parfit gentel knight.

The following evening I went for a long walk to sort out my views, and in my absorption walked too far and consequently had to hurry back through Linton's deserted streets. It must have been after ten o'clock because the pubs were closing.

Then with a leap of the heart I saw four young lads walking towards me, their shadows lengthening grotesquely in the blue light from the street lamp. They must have had a good night at the pub and were making their raucous way home, trying to sustain the conviviality that the beer had loaned them.

There was no escape. I walked quickly towards them, almost sobbing with nervousness and embarrassment, my heels clicking loudly on the pavement.

One of the lads saw me and swayed to a standstill, playfully holding out his arms to prevent my passing.

'Good evening,' he said in a slurring voice. 'Where are *you* off to?'

He tried to catch hold of me but I darted past. He was laughing and I could smell the beer on his breath. The others were gathering behind him.

Like a flash I swung the book I was carrying and clumped it down hard on his head. As I fled to safety, my arms tingling with the shock of the blow, one of the lads had the last word.

'Thoo's safe enough,' he yelled through the darkness and I laughed as I sped back to home and safety.

Yes, I was safe – Jane and John Willy Dobson had seen to that.

11. Back to Work

WHEN he was sixty-three, after having received Public Assistance for
ten years, a miracle happened to Father.

Every Tuesday he made his trip down to Birley Labour Exchange to
sign on. He made an occasion of it, for he met most of his cronies there,
and came back with all the gossip. He usually managed to return with
at least one momentous piece of news, and if nothing spectacular had
happened, he surmised. Mother looked forward to his return and
greeted him with a lively air of expectation, putting up her 'listening'
face all ready to receive his news. Father never disappointed her.

'Guess what's happened now,' he'd cry.

The news varied in importance, but it always received the same
build-up treatment. Once it had been a real tit-bit. Charlie Smith, an
ambitious and civic-minded neighbour, a great bringer home of over-
time pay, had actually had the presumption to stand as Independent
candidate in the local council elections. From time immemorial, we
had returned an all-Labour council unopposed.

'Never the world,' said Mother, correctly impressed by Charlie's
folly.

'Aye, it's reet enough,' returned Father with gloomy satisfaction.
'They'll have to hold a proper election noo and come roond canvassing
for votes. They'll not be returned unapposed this time.'

He sat down, giggling a bit at Charlie's nerve.

'Will you vote for him, Da?'

Father suspended operations with his clay pipe and regarded me with pity.

'D'ye think I'm not reet in the heed?' he asked solemnly. 'A've been a Labour man all me life, as you well know. And I've never had any time for Charlie Smith. He's had the rough edge of my tongue many a time – him and his crackpot notions. But I'm pleased he's standing for the cooncil.'

I looked baffled, so Father explained.

'Mind you, I won't vote for him. Nor will anybody else if they've got any sense. But it'll just show the cooncil members that they cannot have it all their own way. They'll have Charlie to reckon with this time.'

Sure enough, we had a proper election for the first time in years. All the usual Labour members were re-elected, but they hadn't got in un-opposed. It was a triumph for democracy. Father had a grand time going to meetings and heckling the candidates, waxing eloquent about 'jobs for the boys'.

For Father was a man of unbending principle, who had no illusions about human nature. He was a foundation member of the Labour Party and recalled the days of Keir Hardie with pride. For bureaucracy he had an uncompromising dislike. He regarded it as a menace to the freedom of the individual. For him, it was symbolized by the council.

One of Father's favourite pastimes was to watch council employees at work – road-menders, crossings-sweepers, dustbin men or white-collar officials – and to pass caustic comments on their idleness and inefficiency. He knew the private affairs of every official on the council and watched like a broody hen for signs of nepotism. If any local citizen obtained work for the council, Father would find out the whys and wherefores. He regarded a council job as a sinecure, the working-class equivalent of being kicked upstairs to the Lords. It was either given in payment of services rendered to a councillor, or used as a bribe to sweeten a recalcitrant member of the electorate.

Any snippet about the council's doings was brought back triumph-antly and laid before Mother, who shared Father's outlook because he was her pipeline to life.

More usually he'd return from his Labour Exchange sortie with the familiar query, 'D'ye know who's deed?' and he would shake his head with knowing glee as she ticked off their older acquaintances. It was a great day when Father reported the death of a contemporary. Mother had a special face to receive news of this kind, a solemn dignified expression in which the eyebrows were called upon to play their part. When she'd guessed correctly, the two of them would cluck shocked noises of sympathy, overlaid with a guilty patina of delight that they had outlived another contemporary.

Father never failed to bring her back some momentous news from the Labour Exchange trip. Only once did I see him fazed, and that difficulty he surmounted with aplomb.

'You'll never guess what's happened, Jennie. Terrible thing,' he mouthed importantly, and into her expectant ear he intoned with suitable solemnity, 'Oldchester's declared war on Greenlaw.'

But on this particular day he didn't respond to Mother's air of eager expectation. He was too stunned; his voice was flat.

'What do you think, Jennie?'

Mother cocked her head on one side and paled.

'What on earth's happened, Joe?' She sensed a change.

'I've got work.'

The words were dropped nakedly into the air and the two of them stared as if they could see them written there. 'A job.'

Mother had expected a different evidence of the miracle of their survival, and her face looked completely blank. There was no expression in her repertoire to fit news of this magnitude, so baldly presented.

'Job?' she repeated wonderingly, until the word lost its meaning, then sharply, '*Work?* What work is that, Joe?'

The only time Father had been offered work, twelve months ago, an unpleasant scene had ensued. A good many younger miners had been thrown out of work when the Charley pit closed down. Most of them had gone off to the Midlands to try their luck there, but the old ones, who were no longer capable of the physical feats of their youth, were on the scrap heap. 'Redundant' was the term used by officials; 'bloody useless' was how they thought of themselves.

On that occasion Father, preparing to sign on, found himself being cross-examined by the new clerk, young, bespectacled and pale. All the other clerks knew Father, but to this young spelk he had to prove his right to public assistance.

'Have you genuinely tried to get work?' he was asked.

Father opened his mouth and turned to the group of useless old men behind him, rolling his eyes upwards to indicate the clerk's stupidity.

But the huddle of old dependants slumped their shoulders and avoided his gaze.

'D'ye think,' Father tackled the clerk, 'that if there was work to be had I'd be cluttering up this office?'

The young man's lips twitched in the impersonal smile of the official.

'There *is* work to be had,' he answered softly. 'I've a job for you.'

'Doon the pit? At my age?'

'No. Your doctor's certificate says that you are no longer fit enough for heavy manual work.' The tone tried to appear fair.

'Well, what have you got for me?'

The clerk referred to an official form.

'They need men to sweep out factories in Sheffield,' he said. 'Light manual work. You can do that.'

There was a silence which the clerk interpreted as acceptance. He pushed form and pen towards Father.

'You can save your breath. I'm not taking it.'

Surprise appeared on the clerical features, and the young man behind the official mask flushed with annoyance.

'Are you refusing the offer of employment?'

There was a frightened silence among the old men waiting in the queue behind Father, then a nervous shuffling of feet.

'I'm not going,' said Father mildly. 'And that's flat.'

'On what grounds?'

'Me feet's crippled with rheumatism,' explained Father with dignity. 'And you've offered me a standing job. I couldn't do it. And I've got no intention of leaving me family, neither.'

'Your feet seem to carry you down here every week,' snapped the youngster. He took up an office stamp and banged it on the violet pad. He seemed genuinely indignant that an unemployed man was actually refusing a job. 'There's too many like you, drawing dole, that's not willing to work.'

Father's voice was deceptively mild, but his fingers were trembling.

'I didn't say I wasn't willing to work. I said that the work you offered me wasn't suitable.'

'And what work *could* you do?'

The clerk's tone held a sneer. At that moment he was the taxpayer, contemptuous of the social parasite. Power is often put into strange hands.

Father's nobbly forefinger stretched out until it almost touched the insolent clerical face.

'I could do *thy* job,' he said.

He never had any more trouble at the Labour Exchange, but the insult to his manhood rankled. I'd sometimes catch him feeling the muscles that ten years ago had flexed with a hewer's skill, but now lay slack and flabby. He'd force his puffy feet into his old pit boots and prance around the back-yard path, wincing with pain.

'In me prime,' he'd say to me, 'I was one of the best hewers at the Charley. Noted for it,' and then would follow a tale of drama down the pit. He dwelt on stories of accidents and explosions, of men trapped in the darkness, helpless under the weight of fallen pit props. He himself had been a rescue worker in the big Charley disaster, had taken on his back the weight of a fallen beam while men were dragged out beneath.

'How I did it I'll never know. Couldn't raise me arms properly for weeks afterwards. Aye, a terrible thing it was at the time. A terrible thing for Rainton. I was one of the lucky ones.'

And his face would grow grey and pinched.

Sometimes, in a gay mood, he'd tell me of the time a ceiling of coal fell in, closing off his Uncle Albert's way of escape.

'A funny fellow Albert was. Used to make you laugh. Comical with it. I heard him tell the tale many a time till he had us bad with laughing.'

The resourceful Albert had been more concerned with his canary than with a realization of the danger he was in.

'That was before they got the Davy lamps you see, lass, in the olden days. They tested for gas with canaries, but they were grand company forby that. Albert was particular attached to his un.'

Albert, when the seam fell in, had knocked a way through to another seam, long disused, and had followed the narrow tunnel until he saw light coming from above.

'He shoved the cage up first, you see, with the canary in it. He wanted it to get a breath of fresh air, 'cos their lungs is powerful small.' Father spat, then went on. 'All of a sudden the cage is snatched out of his hands and everything goes black. Then there's a queer rumbling noise and Albert, who's a bit light in the head by now, thinks the end of the world is coming.

'Then he thinks to himself it's now or never, so he heaves himself up to see what's happened to his canary. He can hear these voices coming from a lang way away and he's willing to take a bet on it that it's either Old Nick himself or the rescue workers. So up he gets, prepared to give a piece of his mind to whoever he finds up above.

'Next thing he knows, he's climbing out of a well in a village about two miles away from the pit. There's a woman standing there with a bucket in one hand and his canary cage in the other, and when she sees Uncle Albert coming out of the well – and a proper sight he must have been, all black with his pit-clothes riven to bits – she lets out a shriek and runs off saying the devil is after her. It turns out she's a chapel woman at that.

'Albert said that he never forgot the sight of her face when she seed him. He was jabbering aboot his blessed canary and she must have thought he was cussing her to smithereens.

'Just shows – she cannot have had an easy conscience, chapel or no chapel.'

Father's collection of pit stories had for me the compulsion of the old Norse sagas, but for him they were a reminder of his dignity as a man. Yet despite his pride in telling of his former skill, each story reminded Father of his present helplessness. It seemed as if he would never work again. And now came this miracle!

Mother's voice was sharp as she repeated her question. 'What work have they given you, Joe?'

'Sweeping the roads. For the *cooncil*,' Father yelled, prancing into mime, pulling his face about grotesquely. Mother laughed delightedly.

'After all the things you've called the council,' she said, wiping her eyes. 'For *them* to take you on.'

Father had the grace to look ashamed. Now the boot was on the other foot. Father's entering municipal employment made a great change in our life at home. For the first time for years we could make ends meet. That Sunday evening ritual gained a new significance. Real money was coming in.

Father and Mother would sit down at the table and out would come the bottle of ink and the amber pen with the 'J' nib. Mother would importantly produce the Store bill and the Store Club book, the only kind of credit that was regarded as decent. Nobody is more ashamed of 'tick' than the unemployed. If you couldn't pay, you did without. But the Store Club was different because you were a member.

Then Father would make two lists, one of absolute necessities, the other of things we could cut down on. School uniform for Alice and me and money for Ted's textbooks went on the first list, household goods on the second.

On the fortnightly Store bill, Father's half ounce of twist baccy appeared regularly, even during the bad times. Mother was a reasonable woman and knew her duties as a wife. A husband's self-respect must be preserved.

Her own self-respect was boosted in a different way. She rarely went out of the house, but when she did she looked trim and smart. Her fondness for emphasizing her natural good looks, coupled with lack of money, combined to create a flair for clothes. She had a talent for making over old hats. She'd steam them and pull them about into new shapes, then select from her hoard of feathers, veils and artificial flowers *the* eye-catching adornment. She had the magician's trick of diverting the onlooker's attention from what she wanted to hide – the shabby old coat and stitched shoes – to the freshness of her complexion and the sparkle in her eye. Her back was always straight and her head held high.

'It's no good being poor and looking poor,' she'd say, grasping the handle of her gamp (never opened because the ribs had long ago worn through the covering) and preparing to brave the eyes of a hostile world.

Now that she had Father's weekly wage through her fingers, she put aside the money that should have gone towards a winter coat for herself to be used instead for Ted's books. The boy should have his chance.

After leaving school, Ted had been serving his apprenticeship at the garage just over the crossings. He wore an oily overall during the day, so there wasn't much wear and tear on clothes. He was proving expensive in another way – he was ambitious. At work he loved tinkering about with engines, and after hours he found his passion for mechanical things needed other outlets. He was driven by a desire to discover how things worked. Three evenings a week he attended a course of night classes at Birley, but instead of satisfying him, it seemed to unsettle him. Of late he'd become moody and withdrawn. Without appearing to notice, Mother was secretly worried about him and when Jane came home for a week-end, Mother asked her to tackle him.

Jane sent Alice and me off to the cinema matinée, where we inflamed our imaginations with the Clay Men in the serial, and when Father went along to 'the seat', Mother went upstairs to turn out the big wooden box. Jane and Ted had the living-room to themselves, a matter which always required great organization.

She came directly to the point. As the person who provided Ted with his five bob a week pocket-money, she had the right.

'What's on your mind, Ted?'

A thin sliver of afternoon sun made a lace-curtain pattern on his face, as he lay slumped on the couch under the window. Ted surveyed the twinkling dust motes with a studied air of concentration, and didn't answer.

'Nothing, eh?'

Ted shrugged, curling his full lips into a grimace.

'There's plenty the matter with your manners.'

Jane's tone was sharp. Ted flushed and half sat up.

'Manners?' he said. 'We can't afford manners.'

Jane waited.

'We can't afford a bloody thing.'

Jane's breath hissed in, then she let him have it.

'That's a fine way to talk, Ted Craddock. We all do the best we can for you. You get books, don't you – and pocket-money? You should thank your lucky stars you're not down the pit. You've got a lord's life in comparison to theirs.'

Ted slammed the flat of his hand down on the arm of the couch, making the dust motes dance dizzily.

'I'm not complaining,' he yelled thickly. 'I'm not saying anything, am I?'

Seeing the frustration in his widened eyes, Jane softened.

'I'm sorry, Ted. It's not easy for you. I thought you didn't understand our circumstances, that's all.'

'I've understood nothing else ever since I can remember. I've grown up with them. I've had them rammed down my throat.'

After a pause, Jane repeated softly, 'We do the best we can.'

Ted grinned up at her. He had a nice grin.

'I know that as well. I'm not blaming you. I'm not blaming anybody. It can't be helped.'

He bent his head and looked down at his hands, rubbing them together with locked-in violence, and something about the narrowness of his young shoulders touched Jane.

'You'll have your chance, Ted,' she said coaxingly. 'In another couple of years Father'll be on the old age pension and that'll be the end of the dole. It'll all be different then. I'll come and live at home and maybe by then Alice will have a job. Things will be better – you'll see.'

She tried to inject some optimism into the rapid words, but Ted wasn't fooled.

'The lecturer at the Tech. wants me to go in for a full-time course,' he told her. 'Says I have a flair for mechanics, but I haven't got the training.'

The pride in his voice changed to bitterness.

'There's so much to learn, Jane. And I can't study at home. Besides, I need some decent equipment.'

He looked straight at her and spoke with forceful sincerity. 'I wish to God I'd never started the classes.'

Jane searched for some consolation to give him, but there wasn't any. We just couldn't afford to send Ted full-time to the Tech., not with two girls still at school.

'I'll speak to Father about it,' she promised, but Ted shook his head.

'No, don't. It's no use. He'd only blame himself and he does the best he can. Funny how those words keep cropping up.'

She made a final effort to jerk Ted out of his despair.

'Something *will* crop up. You'll see. 'We'll manage somehow.'

Two weeks later, Father was sweeping the roads, employed by the council, but reserving his right as a free-born individual to maintain his critical attitude towards it. He made a clear-cut distinction between regular municipal employees and 'us temporaries'. It was clear that the temporaries brought efficiency and public-spirited zeal to the service. At home the main topic of interest was how greatly the condition of the roads had improved since Father had given them his attention.

'Aye, a road's a funny thing,' he'd say. 'It may *look* clean, but them that knows would soon tell you different. There's a bonny lot to road-sweeping.'

Or he'd tell Mother, 'It's a downright shame the way them roads has been neglected,' and she'd nod, impressed.

A regular wage was coming into the house now and she could actually put a bit by without worrying in case 'they' found out. Free-dom suited her. It was a great day when Father gave her a ten-shilling note 'for yourself noo, Jennie' and she went off to the 'toon' with Jane to buy a hat, delightfully scared at the extravagance.

For Father, work was the best tonic in the world, and he exacted its full compensations from us all. For Father was a Victorian to the back-bone. He knew how the breadwinner was to be treated. He'd come in from work, sit in his wooden armchair and demand service. His boots had to be pulled off, his cap and scarf hung behind the door, his mug of tea ready as he liked it, hot, strong and sweet.

'There's no need to pinch the tea noo,' he'd complain. 'What do you call this? It's blash – watter bewitched and tea begrudged.'

Before he went off to work in the morning Mother would have blackleaded the grate and lit the kitchen fire. Alice and I would tend to Father, fetch his breakfast, lay out his brushed work clothes and hand him his bait tin and tea flask. We took it in turn to clean his boots because 'us temporaries has to set a good example to the cooncil men'.

At home he had first refusal of any food in the house, and his bath water had to be drawn for him. We all must walk on tiptoe and talk in hushed whispers when he was taking forty winks, and his judgement had to be sought on every topic.

The homespun philosopher, detached from the affairs which distract men's objectivity was gone. Instead we had a martinet for a Father. Mother loved it. It was, 'Yes, Joe,' and 'What do you think, Joe?' and to us, 'You'd better ask your father.'

If powerful, he was also just. Practically the first thing he did was to see that Ted enrolled for the full course at the Tech.

'Take a tip from your father,' he told him. 'Stick in and mak summat of theeself, son.'

'I'll never doubt the Craddock luck again,' grinned Ted.

While we all basked in his reflected glow, Father was widening his horizons. His talk became rougher, his gestures more manly. He hobbled with a swagger now and cooled his tea in his saucer unchecked. He had a grand time as man of affairs.

Occasionally he caught me grinning at him ironically and once he gave me back a conspirator's wink, but in general it didn't do to comment on the change in him. Like a true man of the boards he submerged himself in the part, acting for all he was worth.

In the mornings as we rattled past the cross-roads in what was grandly referred to as the 'Scholar's bus', Alice and I would wave to him. The municipal cart would be standing there and Father next to it, casting a professional eye on the gutters or studying the state of the weather. When the bus came past he'd grasp the broom handle with a flourish and studiously ignore our fluttering hands. Men of the council, his back implied, had weightier affairs on hand than acknowledging family ties.

After work, with his pipe going nicely, Father would regale us with snippets of gossip, social criticism and shrewd guesses based on observation. A road sweeper sees a lot of life, being in a privileged position to observe human nature in action when it thinks itself un-observed.

'There's a fella in Trelaw Gardens,' he'd say, 'carrying on with the lass that works in the fish shop. And him a married man.'

Or, 'The ambulance called at Coronation Street this morning – number ten. Looks like twins to me.'

Or, 'Dick Peterson's off work, drawing his sick money and there's nowt the matter with him.'

Or, 'D'ye know who's deed?'

As his marra, Father had Tom Snowdon, a fragile old man with a flourish of good manners and a charmingly archaic way of speaking. Folks called him 'Daft Tom' and indeed he talked little sense, but he was so willing and pleasant an old man, so ill-fitted to face the chaos of life, that Father acted as his protector. It was a case of the lame helping the blind. For, though he concealed the fact from us, Father's feet were in a dreadful mess. Every step he took was agony.

Tom was touchingly grateful when Father, having insinuated himself into the good graces of a sympathetic householder, would conduct him into the kitchen where there'd be a pot of tea for the two of them.

When they were on the roads, one sweeping while the other trundled the cart, Father would push Tom into the foreman's hut and tell him, 'Had your pipe a few minutes while I do Kimberley Street.' Then Father would toddle off on his shaky old pins to do the work for both. From the practice old Tom gained a rest and Father a reassurance of manly vigour and the foreman winked an eye.

'An eddicated chap, that foreman,' Father startled us by saying. 'Pleasant spoken chap, not like some. Aye, he's got his head screwed on right.'

This was a departure from his usual attitude to authority. Was Father mellowing with age or was he turning conformist? Then I realized that the foreman's chats took place in working hours. Father was merely being diplomatic returning a compliment for a privilege.

Every morning the old tin bath was brought into the living-room for Father to steep his feet. It was a ritual, Mother being the grave dame bearing healing salts and fresh water for her travel-stained Odysseus. His weary old feet were taking a beating but Father wouldn't give in to the pain he suffered. When the weather turned cold and the leaves fell, there was more work for him, but when winter brought snow which quickly turned to icy grey slush, his job became a nightmare. Still he wouldn't admit defeat. He wasn't going to give up a regular job, even though his mittened hands froze to the shovel handle.

'I'm not frightened of a bit cold,' he'd snap as Mother pinned an enormous muffler round his chest. 'All this fuss about nowt.'

He put on a bold front, but his back was the bent back of an old man.

After the worst of the winter was over, the council had an economy drive and cut down on road sweepers. Younger men could do the work more quickly and efficiently, so they didn't have to employ so many. Once more Father was on the scrap heap, his Indian summer of employment was over.

'It's Ted I'm worried aboot,' he confessed. 'We'll have to get our thinking caps on. He cannot give up his chance noo.'

Then Alice startled us all by confessing that she wanted to leave school.

'What about your Senior Oxford?' Mother was appalled.

'I don't think I'll pass.'

'Rubbish. You're talking out of the back of your neck,' said Father with vigour. 'The Craddock hasn't been born that couldn't pass an exam.'

In bed, I questioned Alice about her decision.

'What are you going to do if you don't take your exam?'

'Work in a shop.'

I was impressed, but dubious. Jobs weren't easy to get.

Alice burst out: 'I'm sick to death of seeing Father knocking himself out for us. It's time we did our share.'

I hadn't thought about it from that angle. We were 'the bairns'.

'And you should help Mother more, our Mary.'

I was stung. 'I make the bed and help with the washing-up. And I run errands.'

Alice stroked my hair apologetically.

'I know you do. It's just that I worry about them. With Jane away, *I'm* the eldest daughter at home. It's my responsibility. I want to do *my* bit.'

I leaned over to look at her. A light seemed to shine on her face. I was troubled.

'You see, Mary, you don't remember how bad things can get. I don't really, but I've heard them talk about the big strike, when they many a time had nothing to eat.'

In the silence I fidgeted. It seemed a long time before Alice spoke again, this time with fierce intensity.

'If I can see any way of helping out, I'll do it. We've got to try to pull ourselves out of this hole.'

'Eh?' What was she driving at?

'Rainton.'

I'd never thought of Rainton objectively. I accepted it as the place where I lived, pit-chimneys, slag-heaps and all. There was a local superstition that worse places than Rainton existed. We referred contemptuously to *Linton* as 'the last place God made'. I repeated the local phrase tentatively to Alice, in utter sincerity.

'There's this to be said about Rainton – it's easy to get out of.'

There was a new bitterness in Alice's laughter.

'I hate Rainton,' she said fiercely. 'It's a one-eyed little hole. And I for one am going to get out of it.'

Her voice carried much more conviction now than when she had been mouthing phrases about helping the folks.

I was lost, floundering. What was happening to the family? One of my earliest beliefs, as inevitable as bread and jam, was that whatever happened, the family must never split up. It was too self-evident to be questioned. And here was Alice, of her own accord, suggesting that she should leave it. She went on eagerly.

'If I can't get a job in a shop, without my Oxford, then I'll go to a training centre. One of the girls at school went and she's a cook now, in a big house. I'll go down south. She says they like girls from the north there, because they're better workers. I'll put so much by every week to send home, so that Ted can finish at the Tech.'

Her rapid flow of words washed over me, but I'd ceased to listen. I had been introduced to the idea of responsibility – or rather the familiar old word suddenly fattened out with meaning and grew arms to grab me. Father and Mother were getting old – they, the ageless ones – and somebody would have to look after them. Alice was going away – I accepted that fact as if it were already accomplished – then I should be the only one at school. Childhood was nearly over.

Mother, the undemonstrative, gave Alice a peck of a kiss and straightened her hat before, suitcase in hand, she went through the front door for the last time. She would come back for visits, frequent at first – then dropping off – to stop altogether as her new life claimed her. To all intents and purposes we were bidding good-bye to Alice. Already she looked a stranger in her best coat – grown-up and beyond our reach. I said good-bye to her almost with indifference.

Mother shut the front door, then sighed, pulling her cardigan closer round her shoulders. She seemed to feel the cold more these days.

'Well, Alice has gone off now. I had better things in mind for her than washing other folks' dishes.'

Father put his arm round her shoulder.

'It's what she wants, Jennie,' he told her. 'And it'll make things easier for us.'

'Aye, it'll be one less mouth to feed.'

There was a world of bitterness in her voice. Or was I just noticing the undercurrents which before I'd taken for granted, as I'd accepted Rainton?

'There's only the bairn now,' Father smiled at me, and Mother looked towards me, with bright intensity. Her voice lifted.

'Aye, there's still the bairn left,' she said, and her face suddenly looked younger.

12. A New Threshold

FATHER had promised that something should be done for Ted, so there was a family conclave. When Jane come home at the end of term, they discussed Ted's future. Father would draw the dole until 'they' put him on to the old age pension, and awarded him the princely sum of ten bob a week. Financially we'd be worse off, but psychologically Father was looking forward to the day when the authorities would cease to regard him as 'unemployable' and officially designate him as being too old for work. It was an honourable discharge without any stigma of shame attached to it.

The problem of Ted's future was complicated by a new development in Jane's outlook on life. Jane had seemed to fit so snugly into a mould of her own choice that when she began to behave like a normal woman we blinked with as much surprise as if Nipper had given birth to puppies. We'd docketed Jane as hard and dependable, a slave to duty and principles. She was 'the good daughter' whereas Fred was 'the bad son'.

And now this black and white cataloguing was shown up for the over-simplification it was, and Jane's instincts as a human being pushed irresistibly through the self-imposed bonds of self-discipline much as a crocus or snowdrop will force its fragile but determined way through

146

frozen earth. And her flowering was as lovely as theirs. For Jane bloomed as only a girl in love can bloom.

She was being courted by her landlady's son. Henry was an N.C.O. in the Regular Army and he and Jane made plans about the future they would build together when he came out of the army and Jane had fulfilled her obligations to 'see Ted through'. If Henry did not share Jane's optimism he kept his own counsel, but often when she was talking about the house they would eventually buy, a sad smile of wistful longing would soften Henry's tough features. He brooded about politics, not as Father did, with joyous participation, but with a weighty deliberation that was more disturbing. He and young Ted seemed to share a dark instinctive knowledge that coloured their outlook and made them moody in the same way.

Towards Jane, Henry was kind and protective, coaxing her out of her jaundiced attitude to marriage with consummate understanding, letting her take her time and become used to him. As for Jane, she stopped being a rock for us to rest on, and rested in her turn on Henry's strength. There was an understanding at home that when Ted was through the Tech., then Jane's obligations would be finished and it would be Ted's turn to see me through.

Needless to say, Father had forbidden Jane to bring her intended to the house, so Henry's visits were surreptitious.

'Plenty of time for that,' he said flatly. 'Anything might happen. Wait till Ted's got qualified afore you talk aboot throwing yourself away on some man. You might change your mind afore that.'

He still clung to the idea that nobody was good enough for a Craddock. Mother held her peace, secretly sharing his opinion, but too tactful to say so openly. She expected, but was too proud to ask for, Jane's contribution.

Jane was saving up for her bottom drawer and fretted against the weekly drain on her purse. She had a personal interest in Ted's future.

'What about Cousin Albert giving us a hand with Ted's expenses?' she asked out of the blue one day. 'He's on his own now and getting on in years. Surely he must have a nice little nest egg put by?'

Since Aunt Brigit's death, Cousin Albert had lived all by himself in the big house at Conley Bridge. He had followed in his father's footsteps and held a responsible position at the Steel Works. He'd never married, and was reputed to be fussy, old-maidish in his habits as a result of being tied to Brigit's apron strings. He had been 'nooled down' by his mother, who had decided that one profligate in the family was enough. After the wedding, Hettie had been completely cut off from her family. Albert, carrying on the tradition, had neglected to inform Hettie of her mother's death until a week after the funeral.

Father didn't like Jane's suggestion of asking Albert for help.

'We've never been beholden to anybody all our lives,' he stated flatly. 'And I'm blessed if we're going to start now.'

Mother looked at it differently. She, who scrimped to make ends meet, couldn't afford a high moral attitude when Ted's future was at stake.

'It wouldn't do any hurt, Joe, and it might do some good.' Adding to placate him, 'It's still inside the family. It's not as if we were borrowing money from a total stranger.'

Father was talked round. He no longer had the same say in family matters ever since he had gone back on the dole. It wasn't that he was treated with less respect, it was rather that the effort of working again had used up all his reserves, frightening him with his slackened grip. He was putting on the old man a bit now, marking time until he qualified for the old folks' pension. Every day he'd walk along to 'the seat', a covered bus shelter at the end of the street, which had been appropriated by the old pitmen of Rainton. Rain, sleet or shine, the old regulars would collect there, muffled up against the weather, to make slow witannical pronouncements about how times were changing, mourning the diminishing respect that was accorded them by the young folks.

So Ted had to cycle up to Conley Bridge to sound out Cousin Albert. He was received in the kitchen, but offered no refreshments. From the beginning his position was made clear.

Ted didn't even get round to introducing the purpose of his visit. Albert didn't give him a chance. He talked all the time. About himself. About his position in the firm, his prowess on the violin, the unreliability of the woman who 'did' for him. He gave his views on marriage, on how a youngster should defer to his elders, on the possibility of war, on the importance of neatness in dress, on how to avoid avoirdupois.

Finally, as a mark of special condescension, he'd taken Ted into the garden. Walking to the eastern hedge, he placed his finger on it.

'All this is my land,' he said, smiling strangely. 'From here' – then he took Ted over to the western hedge – 'to here.'

Ted hadn't waited to hear any more. He'd got on his cycle and trundled home at a furious rate and burst in upon us in the kitchen.

'He's barmy,' he shouted, red faced. 'Completely off his rocker.'

Mother, when she understood what had happened, shook her head in amazement. Father said nothing. He didn't need to. He brought up his own suggestion.

'I've heard tell,' he began solemnly, 'aboot a thing they called a Special Grant.'

We listened attentively, for Father was talking in 'polite pitmatic', which meant that it was serious.

'It's for the sons of miners, to put them through college and such-like. All you have to do is to gan before this committee and state your circumstances. And if they're satisfied you've got the ability, they'll award you this grant.'

Ted looked at him like a wary animal.

'And then what?'

'Then they'll advance you the money.'

'Sounds like the Means Test to me.'

Father spoke sharply. 'It's the *miners* I'm talking aboot, not the bloody government, lad. Men that understands how we're held.'

'All right,' agreed Ted finally. 'I'll give it a try. It'll do no hurt.'

The experience that followed, though marked with success, made on Ted an ineradicable impression. Beneath his adolescent bluster, he was crawlingly shy.

'It was horrible,' he told me afterwards. 'Going in front of that committee, having to convince them that they weren't chucking good money away if they spent a bit on me. I wish I could have told them what they could do with their ruddy money.'

Father had been in his element. He'd seen beneath the mask of pompous officialdom to the clumsy good nature of men like himself who wanted to help these youngsters but were afraid of being taken in, protecting themselves from fraudulent supplicants behind a hard business-like layer.

Father crowed over their success, not noticing Ted's look of betrayal.

'Aye, it's reet enough. It's the poor that helps the poor. Well, you've got your chance, lad. Make the most of it.'

All this had made a deep impression on me. *I* wouldn't go through Ted's shameful experience. I shared his cringing hatred of asking for something. I made up my mind that I'd either win a scholarship to the local university or get a job in a shop. My aim was so fantastically high that its very impossibility was a challenge. Every night, when I'd finished swotting, I'd walk up the steep bank just outside Rainton, then pause to look down at the glittering village below. And there, on the bank top, I'd solemnly repeat my pact aloud to the stars – then turn and run back down the bank full pelt into Rainton and home. Like Ted, I'd had a bellyful of charity. Pride insisted that I should demand a place because I'd deserved it.

This, then, was my personal obsession, running like a bright ribbon threading together my last terms at school. I was strangely insulated against national events. It was as though I'd contracted out of society, refusing to admit its claims on me. Ted used to talk to me sometimes about the future, but his talk was incomprehensible to me – men's talk about markets and war machines and foreign cities – because it didn't touch my world.

I began to be increasingly conscious of the fact that the family was breaking up. I found myself preoccupied with the idea of change, furtively curious about signs of age. My childhood, in retrospect, seemed to represent security because we'd all been together, creating the unity of a family. Baking day had been a tremendous affair – a whole batch of bread to last the whole week. And on washing day the whole household had been disrupted. *Something* had always been happening – people had popped in, there had been a succession of crises to surmount. Now all decisions had been made and we were all marking time, uneasily *waiting* for something to happen.

Fred was raising a family, Jane was waiting to be married, Alice was waiting to step into the cook's shoes, Father was waiting for the old age pension, Ted was waiting to qualify – I was waiting for the exam. And Mother, she who had waited patiently all her life, what was she waiting for? I avoided thinking about that, but I realized with a shock that I was the only one left in embryo, unjelled, and therefore was especially important to Mother. When my path lay clearly marked, what then? What would her function be?

I clung to my nebulous state, refusing to grow up. During my last years at school Mother became the object of my fascinated interest, supplanting Father in my hierarchy. Everything about her seemed strange.

I questioned her about her youth, about the clothes she'd worn, the dreams she'd had as a girl. She spoke of things beyond my comprehension, of a life so narrow that I was shocked. What had driven her on, to endure the years of privation and worry?

I wanted to give her the world. Every week I put a few coppers aside towards little presents for Mother – a lipstick, a little brooch, her first pair of ear-rings. She could make the cheapest trinket look beyond value. She had an air, a quality that amazed and delighted me. I flattered her shamelessly in order to hear her laugh and see her tweak her fringe with pride. She was a lovely woman.

'Aye,' Father had repeated for years, 'none of you'll ever be as bonny as your mother.'

And it was true. She'd developed a protective serenity behind the barrier which deafness had set up between her and the world.

I used to catch her paging through the books I brought back from the library – reproductions of paintings, illustrated histories.

'What's the good of them?' she'd say impatiently. 'What are they all about?"

Later I'd find her studying a picture, admiring the costume of a Renaissance lady or clucking disapprovingly over a realistic modern. She had pronounced likes and dislikes.

'There's enough misery in the world without dwelling on it,' she'd say, rejecting the novels of social realism I brought home. 'Next time fetch a nice historical novel back.'

I had left my poetry book open at Hood's 'Take her up tenderly', a poem I liked because it made me feel mushily sad at the misery of rejected youth. To my surprise Mother read the poem. Lines, to me obscurely sad, conveyed to her the familiar sordidness of another girl gone wrong. In her opinion it was no subject to write about. Though I pretended to be amused at her Victorian prudery, I was awed that she had seen so clearly what the poem was about whereas I had felt only a vague adolescent non-understanding.

After Father had made his supreme effort for Ted, he had retired into the world of old men, gone beyond my reach. I tried to interest Ted in my vague fumblings towards a shape. I wanted definite opinions, aims, a meaning to it all, but Ted was dedicated. Every night he sat up late to study, with only the tick of the kitchen clock and the sputter of the dying fire for company. The black cat used to sit on his books or toy idly with his pencils, watching over him like an ageless deity, cutting him off from the rest of us.

At school I searched in vain for a kindred spirit. I felt impatient with the other girls in the Sixth, who had accepted without question their roles-to-be. They looked red-cheeked and happy, cluttered up with hockey sticks, developing special sly smiles as they giggled over boys.

I started watching the teachers, seeing them now as individuals. The three-dimensional reality they acquired when viewed from my new slanting angle, startled me. Everything seemed to be teetering on the verge of a pattern and I believed with fervour that it only needed a little twist of the wrist to bring the whole of reality clearly before me, knowable.

One teacher I watched in particular. Mr. Lane, guiding us nonchalantly towards the exam, letting us sniff at it, familiarly at first then contemptuously as jockeys let their horses sniff at the hedges on which they might founder, seemed to want to touch our lives at a deeper level. For him alone we each seemed to exist separately. He would introduce an idea, a point of view alien to us, hold it before us in his thin fingers, then seem to lose interest in it, throwing it aside for us to pick up if we wished, but making no claims on us.

For some reason I felt, as in a private fetish, that if I could only understand Mr. Lane, then everything else would fall into place. He would be the key of the cipher. I studied him with a mystic intensity, so that he seemed to dissolve and slide away from my over-anxious grasp, only to reappear indestructible and maddeningly as unknowable the next time.

Mr. Lane was a grey man – his suit, his hair, his face were all granite grey and his features were sharp as if they'd been hacked out of the rock. He had a quality of permanence, he could never have been young, nor would he ever age. There was no surplus of rounded flesh to pare off and decay, he was pared to the bone.

Then he died.

His greyness had become tinged with colour, his eyes had grown brilliant. He had been in the last stages of T.B. and had chosen to stay on at his job till the last possible moment.

A quiver of excitement electrified the school. There was to be a funeral – Mr. Lane was to be cremated at Newcastle. All the teachers were going and the head boy and girl were to represent the pupils. The empty formality of the whole ceremony seemed so utterly inappropriate that I felt sickened. Mr. Lane, the least sentimental of men, would have shared my distaste at this orthodox mummery.

For the first time in my life I played truant. I had to get away to think it all out, in complete isolation.

I left the house, carrying my schoolbag as usual, then I walked along by the White Gates, through the woods and past the tower. Regardless of trespassing, I crossed the fields leading to Greenlaw, then I came upon a country lane I'd never travelled before, so on impulse I walked along it, following its meandering way for what seemed miles, before I admitted I was completely lost.

The light drizzle that was falling obscured even the hedges, lending the scenery an unreal air of faery enchantment that fitted my mood. I felt free and strangely detached, wandering through silent fields and along alien lanes until I paused to rest by an old bridge that seemed strangely familiar, as a landmark met in dreams can appear familiar. The area had a neglected look, as if nobody had lived there for many years. From the bridge the road ran sharply up a steep hill and I was curious as to where it might lead. In the quiet of the morning, with my face upturned for the gentle prick of the drizzle, I toiled up the hill.

And so at last I came to Avelstan.

There beside the signpost stood the famous stone where some holy man had preached centuries ago. And it was just a stone, a lump of rock sticking out of the ground, half embedded in moss and ferns. I walked through the village street past the pub where Father had lived as a boy, rejecting it as inadequate, looking beyond it for the colours that Father's imagination had given it. On I went to the village green – a tiny patch of grass beside a derelict barn-like affair that must have been the school, where Father had dazzled all with his brilliance. The cottages were little better than slums, their gardens mere rubbish dumps. The whole village had a weary air as if it were crumbling into disuse, too tired to keep up the pretence any longer, anxious to return to that primaeval state of comfortable formlessness from which man had wrested it in creative frenzy.

I paused by the duck-pond – now a mere puddle, sluggish with sediment – and found myself outside the blacksmith's forge. There was no roof on the building, only the blackened stumps of wooden beams. Perhaps the fire that had destroyed it had been an accident, and the blacksmith, a fatalist, had turned his back on the village and, like Father, had never returned. Or had some half-demented villager deliberately set fire to the smithy, whose uselessness seemed a symbol of the decay of the village itself?

The very air I breathed seemed oppressive and sluggish, fit only to breed such morbid fancies. I turned my back on Avelstan and ran down the bank to the bridge below. I felt a strange protectiveness towards Father as I silently promised never to let him know I'd visited his birthplace.

And now I was alone, as I'd wanted to be.

I leaned over the crumbling parapet, drawn to gaze at the stream below, and the surface of the water seemed to hold a suggestion of the pattern I sought. The death of Mr. Lane, the sight of Avelstan, the

hollow expression behind Mother's eyes – all seemed to have a con-
nexion, to hold a wisdom which I felt intuitively, but failed to understand. Accept this, it seemed to say, and go on from there.

It was as though I had glimpsed the pattern of my life there in the
waters that ran below Avelstan – had glimpsed its essential truth and
accepted its validity. For – and this seemed enormously significant – it
wasn't *just* my life – it was part of the pattern.

The tension dropped from my limbs. I felt strangely at peace and full
of a confidence I hadn't suspected possible. I should go back, lose the
clarity of this vision, but its memory would sustain me as something
like it must have sustained my mother.

So I returned to Rainton and shut myself up in a world of books,
reading widely and indiscriminately, avidly seizing hold of new ideas,
always conscious of Mother's watching eyes behind the hooded lids. I
wrote like an automaton in the exam, disinterestedly, then forgot all
about it.

When the foolscap envelope arrived at breakfast one morning, I
threw its contents in the air, watching the official paper flutter down as
if it had no significance, instead of the power to change my life.

'What is it, Mary?' asked Father fussily, picking up the paper with
clumsy trembling fingers, fearing bad news.

'I've got the Scholarship.'

Father preened himself like a peacock, strutting about and chuckling,
'Aye, you've shown them, lass. You're a fairly Craddock.'

I watched him across a gulf of indifference, waiting for Mother's
comment.

'Well,' she said with a little sigh, 'it's all over now,' and I felt that she
meant more than my schooldays.

'No,' I muttered urgently, shaking my head at her, willing her
to understand, and something of my fierceness got through to her,
for she smiled with unexpected tenderness and put her arm
around me.

'We'll have to try and get you fixed up for college,' she went on in
her brisk practical voice, and I was comforted.

Ted and Jane were delighted at my success, but my brother's
pleasure was tinged with bitterness.

'You'll be all right,' he said. 'But I don't think I'll be able to finish
my course. I started too late.'

Knowledge that I had forced into the back of my mind burst
through.

'So there's going to be a war?'

'Of course.' Ted's tone was almost bored.

Everything that I'd read seemed meaningless in the face of this. Out of all the words I'd burrowed through, only these stuck to my groping fingers:

'These fragments have I shored against my ruin.'

'How soon?'

Ted shrugged. It didn't matter. He would join up anyway. His mood of resignation trickled through to me, then I rejected it. Everything suddenly seemed more significant simply because it might be threatened. I prepared for college life with a frantic zeal. During the summer holiday our house once more buzzed with activity.

We even had a visit from Fred.

Father saw him coming up the path and gave warning. Mother locked herself in the bathroom where she changed out of her working dress and fussed her fringe into curls. Winking at Father, I grabbed an impressive looking textbook and pored over it, pretending to be so absorbed that I didn't realize that Fred had come in.

In the small kitchen he seemed to use up all the air. The muscles he'd developed as a pitman showed lumpily under his jacket.

'What fettle there, Father?'

I remember the strident voice shouting, 'Wash my back.'

Father nodded, looking at the floor. 'Canna grumble,' then – reluctantly – 'Hoo's theself?'

'Canny. We're doing very canny.'

He seemed ill at ease, too big for the armchair.

Father shot him a glance. 'What's on thy mind then, Fred?'

'Nowt. Nowt at all. I just looked in.'

He glared around him as if he'd been trapped, a grimace fixed glassily on his face in travesty of a smile.

Father allowed the silence to become oppressive, then spat into the fire with masterly aim. I flicked at the pages of my book. I could hear Mother in the back kitchen, pulling open the cutlery drawer in the table, then opening the pantry door.

Fred's wandering eye caught mine.

'Well, Mary,' he boomed.

I took pity on him. 'How are the bairns?' I asked politely.

He leaned forward eagerly, making the springs protest squeakily. 'Doris come top of her class,' he told me proudly.

Father breathed out heavily in contempt. He couldn't keep up the pretence any longer.

'And what do you think of our Mary?' he demanded fiercely. 'Passed for the univorsity. With honours into the bargain.'

I had tried to explain the system of awarding scholarships to Father, without success.

As if on cue, Mother, who had stopped rattling cups in the other room, opened the door and reacted with a well-simulated start of surprise on seeing Fred. She came forward with outstretched hand, like a lady at a garden party, and shook his hand formally.

'You're quite a stranger,' she said graciously, then to me, 'Put the kettle on. Fred's just in time for a cup of tea.'

Fred grew red in the face. As Father observed later, you could see Sadie pulling him back by the reins.

'No. Nowt for me,' he roared.

'Had your pipe, Fred. It won't do any hurt to have a sup tea.' Father was firm.

'Well, nothing to eat then.'

The compromise seemed fair enough. Principles were preserved beneath a façade of consideration. Fred sipped at his tea as if it were poison, under Father's malicious eye.

'You'll be off to college I hear,' Fred said to me.

'Yes, in October.'

Father spat pointedly, making the coals sizzle.

'Aye, it takes brains,' was his comment. 'Mary takes after the Craddock side.'

After a pause, he went on innocently: 'Hoo's that bairn of thine doing? Doris, isn't it?'

Fred proudly repeated his information. Father looked surprised.

'Top of the class, eh? Funny thing that. I was just saying to Jennie only the other day that that bairn is the spitting image of Sadie. And she's come top of the class?'

He shook his head in wonder. Mother, with her private radar means of following conversation without hearing them, suddenly chimed in with: 'How is Sadie's poor father getting on?'

The old man had been queer for the last year or so, given to strange fancies and childish behaviour.

Fred flushed an ugly brick red. 'He's all reet. Nowt the matter with him.'

Father's eyes sparkled but his tone was honey soothing. 'It's just old age that's turned his brains a bit. Happens to all of us in time. His father went exactly the same way.'

Fred wasn't anxious to pursue the topic. He got to his feet and pulled a paper parcel from his inside pocket.

'Here. Sadie's sent this alang for you.'

He thrust the parcel into my hands. It contained a hand-knitted scarf, soft to the touch. I felt ashamed, reluctant to accept the gift. Fred however had the last word.

'So's you'll have something decent to wear at college, like.'

Fred was a fairly Craddock too. I grinned at him with something like admiration, while Mother examined the scarf critically, clucking over it, shyly admiring the intricate pattern.

'Sadie must have plenty of spare time on her hands,' Father suggested half-heartedly, but it was no good. The round had gone to Fred. He went off gaily down the path, like a victor.

Father sulked for the rest of the day. Fred had spoilt his thunder. For weeks Father had been making references to some great secret and I knew that something was in the wind. He'd been keeping it back until I set off for college, but Fred's visit had put him off his stroke. Seeing me with the scarf put him into a temper.

'Here,' he said at last, 'take that clarty thing off your neck and gan and hev a look in the top of the press.'

I obeyed, fumbling among the books and cardboard boxes.

'Weel? Have ye foond it?'

My fingers encountered a heavy brown paper parcel. 'Is this it?'

Mother and Father were seated formally at each side of the fireplace while I unwrapped the parcel. Finally I disclosed a huge dictionary. I looked up to see them watching me anxiously.

'Well, what do ye think of it?' asked Father eagerly.

I found it hard to speak. The book was huge and useless. I had already ordered the Oxford Dictionary for my school prize. I felt a spurt of irritation at the waste of good money which I could have spent on a book I really needed. I swallowed.

'It's just what I need,' I managed to get out.

Father pointed out the merits of the book, whose purchase had required much anxious thought. I wondered how much he'd spent on it, feeling sad and guilty, utterly inadequate to receive such a gift.

As I hugged them both I felt that I'd never been further away from them. I was already cut off. My thanks sounded artificial to my own ears. They should have been good-byes.

During that long summer vac. before college began, I had to spend a night or two at St. Alban's College in order to be interviewed by the principal, the head of my faculty and the registrar. There were about twenty of us all together and we eyed each other like wary sheep, hiding behind the bright, affected manner that freshers assume.

While I was staying there, Father had to make one of his trips to Oldchester Miners' Hall for one of the big meetings of official delegates. We arranged to meet during the afternoon, on Palatinate Bridge, then have tea together.

As I stood waiting for him in one of the alcoves in the old bridge, I commanded a famous view of the river. High above the tree-lined banks the western towers of the cathedral soared magnificently. It was a poem in stone and I was awed that men had conceived, then built it. The afternoon held a cloistered stillness in which the singing of the birds wove a pattern that seemed to be reflected in the fan-like tracery of the large sycamore whose leaves spread over the water below. I was enchanted. I had reached my personal Avelstan in Oldchester.

Hearing footsteps I turned and watched Father approaching. He was dressed in his best blue suit, sported a buttonhole and carried his silver-handled stick, but he looked what he was – a man moulded by the pits. Strangely impersonal, I watched his limping progress. In this setting he was incongruous – his sprightly shabbiness like a caricature.

We walked in silence together along the banks towards a seat, and a gulf wider than the river separated us, although Father did not seem to be aware of it. Had I outgrown him or did the indifference I felt mean that I was ashamed of him? I had certainly felt ashamed of my inadequacy during the interviews and with the students. To add to the confusion of my feelings was the dread that this life so nearly attained might be threatened. War was imminent. I could no longer close my mind to it.

Father settled himself comfortably, then took out his old clay pipe. To fit the dignity of the surroundings he started talking in polite pitmatic. I was neither amused nor touched by this show of pride; I was too miserable.

'Aye,' he said, after surveying the flowering river banks with a shrewd eye, 'the dean and chapter seems to be doing their job all reet.'

I made no comment, but Father's appetite for life was strong enough without his needing to share it.

'Look there,' he said, pointing with his stick. 'Thon's a water hen.'

Funny thing seeing one of them here. I mind we had one on the pond at Avelstan.'

I focused on the hen, reviving at his child-like interest. My vision cleared, the day seemed brighter. I was at peace, sitting on the river bank beside my now-familiar father, listening to his rough-gentle voice. So that when he said, 'What's the matter, lass?' I told him.

He heard me out, then sighed and nodded.

'Aye, there's nowt so funny as folks,' he said, prodding the grassy bank with the ferrule of his stick. 'You know, Mary, I've seen a lot in my time, seen all sorts of changes, but there's one thing doesn't change. Daftness.'

His voice strengthened and he fixed his shrewd blue eyes on me, seeing through my affected misery to the loneliness and pride beneath.

'You're acting daft. Worrying your head aboot whether you've got a right to be here. What does it matter what other folks think about you? By gum, I wish I'd had the chance you've got. I'd have shown them all. Joe Craddock would have made them all sit up. D'ye think I've ever cared tuppence what anybody thowt of me? Bar your mother, that is.'

He puffed out an explosive pop of air and rolled his eyes.

'I've made it a rule in life never to take notice of nobody. And that's a fact. Ye asked for my advice and I'll give it you. Get yourself reckoned up, lass.'

He caught sight of the cathedral and pointed to it.

'See thon? Canna miss it, can you? A couple of years ago they wanted a tremenjus sum of money to stop that cathedral from falling into the river. And d'ye know where they got the money from? From the miners, lass, and don't you forget it. Never be ashamed of the fact that your father's a miner. There's none better.'

I gasped. He'd seen through me so clearly. No sympathy to protect my wounded self-love – only a douche of common sense. The familiar advice pricked my false egoism and put me on an even keel.

Father winked at me and his last vestige of strangeness disappeared. His face slipped into focus as my own values had done.

'And mind this,' he said. '*I* never got to be a scholar at Oldchester, though I would dearly love to have been. But it wasn't to be. But, hinny, I'm proud of the fact that a bairn of mine – a fairly Craddock – has managed to do what I couldn't. So remember *that* – and get yourself reckoned up!'

And when he'd pulled himself to his feet and brushed at the creases in his best suit, he didn't look shabby at all. I watched him walk away towards the bus stop, swaggering in spite of his rheumatics and bad feet, making great play with his stick.

And when I turned back along the road to college I straightened my shoulders and swaggered along myself, in tune to the words in my head: 'Get yourself reckoned up, lass. Get yourself reckoned *up*!'